D0524835

Farming in the Clouds

Richard Body

Temple Smith/London

First published in Great Britain in 1984
by Maurice Temple Smith Ltd
Jubilee House, Chapel Road
Hounslow, Middlesex, TW3 1TX

© 1984 Richard Body

This edition is copyright under the Berne Convention. All rights are reserved. Apart from any fair dealing for the purpose of private study, research, criticism or review, as permitted under the Copyright Act 1956, no part of this publication may be reproduced, stored in a retrieval system, or transmitted, in any form or by any means whatsoever, without the prior permission of the copyright owner.

Body, Richard
   Farming in the clouds.
   1. Produce trade
   I. Title
   382'.41   HD9000.5

ISBN 0 85117 251 2
Typeset by Tellgate Ltd, Parker St, London, WC2
Printed and bound in Great Britain at
The Camelot Press Ltd, Southampton

Contents

Preface

For some years now I have been aware of a growing body of evidence that the political pressures on British agriculture are causing great damage. Not least among the final victims of this process will be the farmers themselves, who have been pushed into a kind of agriculture which in the end is bound to let them down. Sooner or later the clouds are going to burst.

In my previous book, *Agriculture: The Triumph and the Shame*, I set out my reasons for this belief. In this new book I look more closely at some of the effects of our present policy, and in particular at its main victims, not only in Britain but throughout the world. One part of the shame is that many of those victims are among the very poorest people of all.

Others have already warned of the threatening clouds. Perhaps the first was Enoch Powell, who told the Shropshire NFU in a speech as long ago as 1971 what would happen if farmers allowed themselves to get entangled in the machinery of politics. His warning made me shake off the accepted wisdom, and since then I have set out to gather evidence for what I am now sure is true. Our house has gradually become overwhelmed with paper – if not exactly mountains, at least insurmountable hillocks. How lucky I am to have a wife as an active partner in what has become a cottage industry. We have been joined by my secretary, Helen Suttill. She too has helped to garner the evidence besides labouring with the ultimate of all chores – re-retyping.

My wife and I have been daily witnesses of one way in which things have gone wrong. We live beside the River Pang, between Reading and Newbury, the river Kenneth Grahame wrote about in *The Wind in the Willows*. The river is different now. The Thames Water Authority, as agent of the Minister of Agriculture in drainage matters, was ordered to spend a further £800,000 on top of the £5,000,000 its own experts in drainage considered was enough. The gentleman in Whitehall knows best, we are told, and the Authority had to comply with the Ministerial decree.

First the trees were felled, including willows that Kenneth Grahame might have known. Then came the dredgers to straighten some of the bends and lower the water table to make stretches of it look more like a scaled down version of the Grand Union Canal than a meandering chalk stream. Lowering the water table is necessary because arable crops like wheat, barley and oil seed rape cannot grow unless the wet lowland is dried out by drainage; and in the valley the larger farmers have been goaded by grants, subsidies and import levies into growing such crops, instead of keeping cattle and sheep. A few of us with smallholdings continue to breed and fatten cattle, and three have dairy herds; and we need a high water table to enable the grass to grow well all through the dry summer months. Also the great variety of grasses and flora that make our cattle fatten into top quality meat cannot flourish on dried out land. Some of the flora have died out and disappeared; and the beef is the poorer for it. Beef from these fields has been, according to the wholesale butchers, the best in a radius of many miles. Our interests are thus, by public policy, put in conflict with those of the other farmers. Some of the wild flowers have gone, others are markedly fewer. Of the birds, the snipe, the peewit and the kingfisher are seen no more and the mallard and the moorhen are many fewer. Removal of the cover along the river bank has taken away the habitat of the otter and the water vole – Kenneth Grahame's 'Ratty'.

All this has come about because public money has been spent for the benefit of one half of the landowners and farmers to the detriment of the other half. The farmers for whose benefit it was done would be the first to admit they would never have spent their own money in this way. As it is, all the wheat they grew last year went to Southampton, then to Cuba, with the aid of export subsidies. I calculate that the subsidies to export this surplus wheat from our part of the Pang Valley have cost us not less than £120,000. The purpose of the subsidies is to support farm incomes: I suspect that these subsidies alone – quite apart from other grants, subsidies and tax allowances – exceed the actual incomes received by those farmers.

To make one poor quality field at the top of the hill capable of growing wheat, the owner drained it with a grant of public money; but the water was drained onto the public highway and then, whenever there was a sudden downpour, the road at the bottom of the hill would flood and become almost impassable. So the County Council closed the road for a month, much to the inconvenience of the public who used it every day, and set about spending a lot more public money on a scheme to cope with the floodwater. The true cost to us of growing wheat in that rubbishy field at the top of the hill and the true cost of getting rid of it to Cuba, must add up to quite a bit. Examples like that, of lane widening, of sewerage schemes for intensive farms and of purifying the water supply polluted by excess fertilisers, of extra public money having to be spent as a result of the present policy, are probably to be found in most parishes in the countryside.

So, here at home my wife and I can witness the constant and contrived change in the wildlife and landscape, and reflect on how much it costs. Then constituents write to me, complaining about the cuts in public expenditure that fall upon our schools and hospitals and postpone yet again the building of a bypass. As I look out of the window, up the Pang Valley, I find it difficult to write back a sensible answer.

Ought we to blame the farmer for what he is doing to the landscape? When we had the system of deficiency payments given to the farmer to make up the difference between the world price and his guaranteed price, he was able to buy his wheat, maize and barley to feed his cattle, pigs and poultry at world prices. The emphasis of British agriculture was therefore on livestock, and because of our climate and the poor soil that covers more than half our land, that was economically sensible. It also made our country a green and pleasant place. Then came the preparations to join the Common Market and we had to abandon deficiency payments and go over to their system of import levies and duties.

The main purpose of the new system was to keep out cheap wheat, maize and barley from countries outside the Common Market, especially Canada and the United States. From then on the farmer has been induced to grow those arable crops rather than keep livestock, and a great change has come over our countryside. Protecting agriculture by means of import levies has suited the rest of the Common Market, but not us. The kind of farming most suitable for our soil, climate and terrain – the kind that made our countryside look as it did – is the very kind of farming penalised by the new system.

Farmers have to work the system given them, so they are not to blame. They have been dragged along by a troika in the form of the Ministry of Agriculture, the leaders of the NFU and the agrochemical industry. In this book I describe why those three are much to blame for what has happened and, moreover, for the nemesis that is coming. There is evidence that the agrochemical industry has had an excessive influence over the Ministry of Agriculture to the detriment of us all and I have marshalled a great deal of it together for a third book to be published after this.

So I throw no stones at farmers. I do not blame my neighbours in the Pang Valley for what has been done. Besides, they are good neighbours and I should be sorry indeed to hurt their feelings.

No one, I keep saying, is more important to us than the farmer. He is important because our lives depend upon him. We cannot live without eating what grows on his soil or drinking the water that passes through it. By no fault of the farmer but because of the pressures upon him to force his soil and stock to yield an ever higher output, both the food we eat and the water we drink are becoming dangerous, and before the end of the twentieth century they will be highly dangerous unless great changes are made in agricultural policy. Upon that rock of certainty stands the case for the public coming to the aid of the farmer.

Of the many farmers and smallholders who have gone out of business, at least two thousand have been in my constituency of Holland-with-Boston. With many of them I have sat in their homes before they gave up the struggle, to hear about the difficulties they could not get over and the handicaps they could not shake off. They were able to grow, acre for acre, more than others with farms ten times their size; but it was not enough. They have influenced me more than they may realise. They have given me their ideas and their votes; and in return I must try to put matters right.

Farming or
Aggro-culture?

1/The Party's Over

When agriculture goes wrong, everything else will. That sweeping generalisation I call – if readers will allow the vanity – 'Body's Law', it being a variation of the better known Murphy's Law. Until North Sea oil came along, farming in its many forms was the greatest part of our nation's economy by any touchstone one could choose. It was, and is still, far more than just another industry. It is the chief source of supply for the only one of our material needs that is truly vital, and it is the mainspring of every activity in the countryside. Only a mere industry, indeed! Shame on its leaders to speak so ill of it!

Because agriculture has been treated as an industry, much has gone wrong. Public policy and public money have been directed to one end – getting our acres to grow more food, regardless of other considerations. The late Dr E.F. Schumacher in *Small is Beautiful* suggested that the management of our land – and by land he included the creatures that lived upon it – should be orientated towards three goals: health, beauty and permanence. Food then comes naturally from it. This view (which I hope pervades this book) is the opposite of what our agricultural policy has sought to achieve in the last two or three decades. Vast sums of taxpayers' money have been spent by the government to goad farmers into getting more food out of the same number of acres. In the early days of price support, after the Agriculture Act 1947 was passed, farmers were found to be spending their higher incomes upon improving their standard of living; public money was going into their pockets and being spent by them on making their farmhouses more comfortable or buying new cars and in other ways which were rather sensible. But this did not suit the policy makers and after 1951 most of the financial aids to agriculture were direct inducements to increase food production. We then

12

had subsidies to use phosphate fertilisers, and in the following years, the principle of subsidising fertilisers was extended to all artificials, much to the benefit of certain chemical companies. A ploughing-up grant was also made available to plough permanent pasture and have it reseeded with temporary grasses, which again benefited certain chemical companies, because farmers were strongly advised to apply their particular fertilisers onto the new varieties of grass. Another new grant at that time was for rearing beef calves. As the years went by, new subsidies were devised to force up the production of food – grants for the removal of hedges, grants to uproot old orchards, grants to plough up hill land (£12 an acre, while on the low land it was £7 an acre), grants for winter keep, grants for land drainage, grants for numerous other things.

All this public money – and hundreds of millions of pounds of it were made available – did very little to help the farmer lead a more contented life, and it was not intended to do so. As production rose, farm incomes tended to go down, and far from attaining Schumacher's three goals, it was having precisely the opposite effect. The health of our soil, our stock and ourselves was impaired, and the beauty and permanence of our landscape diminished. Permanence is not the same as petrification. No one who understands the countryside would suggest that it must always look as it does today. That is a prescription for decay. Permanence is about conservation; and while the conservationist believes there are certain features of the landscape that are so naturally in their proper place that they should remain there permanently, he also believes there are lots of places where the bulldozer should move in.

So, in this book, I am arguing that public money has been spent in the wrong way, that it is economically crazy to go on goading our farmers to produce ever more food at ever higher and disproportionate cost, and that if taxpayers' money is to be given to agriculture, it should be for the purpose of attaining Schumacher's three goals.

Sadly, Schumacher died some years ago, before he had time to enlarge upon this theme. But before his death we collaborated together – with Professor Sir Alan Walters, Enoch Powell, Professor Hillman and others – to produce a symposium *Freedom and Stability in the World Economy* in which we set out the principles to enable the West to remain free and stable. From the chapter on food, I cull one prediction:

The ultimate danger is that the world could return to the conditions of the 1930s when international trade collapsed. The effect is the same whether trade is strangled by competitive import barriers, as during the Great Depression, or competitive export controls which have been the threat in the 1970s. Trade regulation by way of export interferences, whatever their economic motivation, cannot be limited to exports alone. Cause and effect are highly inter-related in a world where more than $500,000 millions in product value is being exported by the nations of the world.

Much of this book is about that danger. Our own agricultural policy concerns ourselves, but it touches the everyday life of millions and millions of other people in other countries far away. Some of them can grow food much more cheaply and efficiently than we can; and they have been forced off their farms. Many more are going very hungry, in a way that probably no one in our own country has experienced. But despite it all, our farming establishment, especially certain Ministers of Agriculture and those who speak officially on behalf of the NFU, have seemed impervious to what has been happening beyond our shores.

When the farming establishment persists in speaking of agriculture as an 'industry', it undermines the argument for the very kind of financial assistance that farmers should have to enable them to conserve and protect the countryside. If someone buys a tractor, it does not matter very much how he decides to treat it. He may leave it out all night in the rain or the snow, because he has persuaded himself that it would be cheaper to buy a new one in a year or two than to build a shed to house it. We may think him rather foolish, but we have no business to interfere. The tractor is a mechanical thing which will one day be useless anyway, and what he chooses to do with it is his business. But what he does with his farmland may indeed be our business in all sorts of ways. The drainage of his fields, the ploughing up of the footpaths, the use of some herbicides, the burning of straw and so on are activities that affect other people; and in the twentieth century it is accepted that the public, through its legislators, can properly interfere when its interests are affected. We ought to look upon our farmland as something far more important than just one of the factors of production, and this importance should be implied in the way we interfere with its use. In marketing what he produces the farmer ought to be treated like any other businessman; but if the legislator decides to interfere with the way he works his land he is entitled to look to the taxpayer for assistance.

Part of the shame of our agricultural policy is that we are treating the farmer in almost the opposite way, and the farming establishment would rather have it this way round. In marketing the food he produces, far from the farmer being treated as a businessman, they want him to be molly-coddled to a degree that no one else is; yet in the growing of the food and the way he treats the landscape they would like the principles of laissez-faire to prevail.

This 'industry' of agriculture has, I submit, taken a wrong turning. It is heading for a terrible crash. Like Concorde, what it has achieved, in a technical sense, is a remarkable triumph; but the achievement has been at a very high cost. At the root of the problem is the way the policy makers – the politicians – have goaded the farmer to increase production to the maximum. They have wanted high output, and since that can only be obtained with high inputs, farmers have been forced to adopt a high-input/high-output system. As I have tried to show, we do not need this higher and higher output: we should strive for lower output and achieve it with lower inputs. We are driving agriculture in top gear. My constant theme has been that we should change down.

No doubt Mr Peter Walker was full of good intentions when he first arrived at the Ministry of Agriculture in 1979. With great gusto and zeal he began to pour public money into agriculture. Not only was production to be pushed up: farmers' incomes were to go up too. Let us see what happened.

What Peter Walker did not realise was that if the high-input/high-output path has been followed for a long time, the law of diminishing returns applies. You must put in a great deal more money for the farmer to receive a higher net income. When the

15

price support system began, in the years 1947-1950, a given input of public money had the effect of raising farm incomes almost by the same amount. For every pound put in, about 90p went into the total income earned by all British farmers. Today their aggregate income rises by less than 30p for every pound put in.

In 1978 (the last full year before Mr Walker became responsible) farmers' incomes were £1,238 millions. To obtain the figure for price support, one has to take the nearest fiscal year (1977-1978), and it totalled £1,061 millions. By 1981, despite price support going up to £1,928 millions, farm incomes actually went down to £1,209 millions. In real terms, the reduction was much worse, of course. Still, farmers' incomes went up considerably in the following year to £1,800 millions, but to secure that increase it was necessary to raise total tax-payers' support to £3,200 millions. So, to get farm incomes increased by less than £600 millions above their 1978 level, support had to go up by over £2,000 millions, giving a ratio of almost 4 to 1.

There are two explanations for this growing ineffectiveness. One is the recurring theme of this book, that the more the government expands agricultural output, the more economically inefficient it becomes. The other is that when large sums of public money are spent to distort the price mechanism, with the avowed intention of trying to help the farmer relative to people in other jobs, it is natural for people with capital to invest to divert part of their capital into the favoured field. Agriculture becomes a good investment, with unearned public money going to swell the return. Farming used to be only for farmers: a price support system has brought in purely financial interests.

By about 1950 the new system was established and was seen to be benefiting agriculture. City institutions (which employ clever people to spot these things) calculated that a modest investment in agricultural land was desirable. From then on, the more public money went into agriculture, the more they have invested in agricultural land. They now know the party is nearly over and the interest in further investment is beginning to wane. In the meanwhile, what they have done is to force up the price of land; and as I have shown elsewhere, the value of all our land is about £64,000 millions more than it should be. Rents have risen accordingly, and are two or three times more than they ought to be; and those who have bought land to farm, just as much as the tenants, have had to force high yields out of their soil and stock to pay the first charge upon their income. Their net return has thus failed to rise as fast or as far as their higher inputs.

When we began the system of price support under the Agriculture Act, 1947, farming was in a low gear; production was low compared with what it is now, and the costs were in proportion. As years went by the political masters – the Ministers of Agriculture – called for ever higher levels of production, culminating in 1979, when Peter Walker became Minister. He immediately pushed agriculture into overdrive and roared the engine. Maximum production was the target. No matter if we produced more food than we could eat; let us export it, and the more the better. That was the motive behind his 'Food from Britain' campaign. Our costs of production being higher than those of other countries outside the Common Market created a little difficulty; those surpluses of food could not be sold abroad unless they were subsidised, sometimes at great cost. For example, both in 1982 and 1983 we grew 5,000,000 tonnes of wheat too much and this vast amount could only be exported with the aid of a subsidy of about £60 a tonne. In one year 240,000 tonnes were despatched to Cuba alone on those terms. Of course neither Cubans nor anyone else would import our high cost wheat unless bribed to do so (for such a subsidy is, at heart, a bribe), but that fact was brushed aside. The money would 'come from Europe', we were told, from the guarantee fund of the CAP. It was to be a way of getting some of our money back; and in fact his policy succeeded in getting twice as much money out of the CAP as before.

Mr Walker, not being himself a practical farmer, may be forgiven for failing to realise that to get the highest output from the land, you must put in the highest and most costly inputs. But every farmer knows that the Good Lord does not treat us like spoilt children, and does not allow us high output with low inputs. This is where the leadership of the NFU in 1979 failed its members. They should have told Mr Walker in plain terms that his target would not be achieved unless his policy underwrote the higher costs that would be required. Instead, they went along with the idea of top-gear farming. Farmers in their thousands went to the banks and borrowed millions of pounds more; their total indebtedness to the banks and other mortgagees went up to an estimated £6,000 millions, where it had previously been less than £2,000 millions.

The price of agricultural land shot up to a record height, and the land itself was forced to adapt to kinds of farming it was not naturally capable of doing. Artificial fertilisers were poured on at record levels; so also were herbicides, pesticides and fungicides. Worse than that, new varieties of seed were developed that could only be grown at high cost, and the established varieties of seed which flourished in low-cost systems were allowed to die out. Our livestock also changed. For example, top-gear dairy farming demands a cow that is able to produce the highest milk yields – the Holstein in place of the Friesian. But such a cow must be fed on the most expensive feed compounds: a Holstein would, quite literally, die within a few months if fed on the low cost hay and even straw upon which the Dairy Shorthorns used to give us their lower yields. This is the terrible dilemma of top-gear farming. It is difficult to change down and impossible to revert to low-gear farming, except after a very long period, perhaps twenty years.

What is so extraordinary is that when they gave their wholehearted support to Mr Walker, the leaders of the NFU seemed to be unaware of that dilemma. As no one else seemed willing to utter a note of caution about the danger of this agricultural policy to farmers, let alone the rest of us, I decided to write *Agriculture: The Triumph and the Shame*. When the book was published, Mr Walker publicly said I was 'unbelievably wrong', and was privately a great deal less charitable in describing both me and my views to journalists. Mr Alick Buchanan Smith, the Minister of State for Agriculture, told an audience that my ideas were 'riddled with fundamental fallacies', and though I tried several times to find out from him what they might be, I failed to do so. The NFU got almost hysterical: my views were 'facile and positively dangerous'. The Country Landowners Association published in their official journal a statement about the book, calling in aid the old dictum of 'lies, damn lies and statistics', spoke of 'an unwarranted libel'. That a warning to farmers can be construed as a libel upon them seems a trifle odd, and as a member of the CLA, I asked the editor whether I might be permitted to give to readers an account of what my views really were. He refused. Yet the CLA includes within its membership many forward thinking and very able farmers. They, like so many others less happily endowed, had become hooked on this high-cost farming, and in the process had borrowed vast sums of money on the security of their land. There are members of CLA who will never be able to repay these debts if the fears expressed in the book come true.

Perhaps we should go back to the immediate post-war years for what may be the reason for this high pitched response to what I had intended to be an expression of serious concern. Both the Agriculture Act and the Bretton Woods Conference came at the same time, and there may perhaps be a connection between the two. Maynard Keynes had persuaded the countries of the free world to fix their exchange rates one with another. From that time forth a phrase was always to be heard in any economic debate. It was 'the balance of payments'. For hundreds of years, statesmen had got along pretty well without mentioning it: their countries imported and exported, and in most cases they allowed their businessmen a fairly free hand in buying and selling abroad whatever they wanted.

Bretton Woods changed all that; the easy tolerance gave way to a mixture of rewards and punishments for those who traded abroad. An exporter was a good guy, an importer a bad guy. Knighthoods and the CBE for exporters; they were applauded at the Mansion House. One Prime Minister declared we must 'export or die,' another told the City 'exporting is fun.' Later on, those who responded to the exhortations were given the Queen's Award. Importers, on the other hand, were regarded very differently. Come a 'balance of payments crisis', which occurred regularly every two or three years, importers were summoned by their bank managers to be told that Head Office was concerned, the Treasury was concerned and 'in the national interest' (a questionable phrase to mean almost anything) the overdraft must come to an end.

Import substitution was talked of now; it too was 'in the

national interest'. As we imported a large part of our food, eyes naturally turned to the farmers to play their part in this great task of rebuilding our economy. The government wanted higher food production; henceforward the farmer was the catspaw of the politician. He still is. And the mischief will continue for as long as that remains the case.

Cosy meetings between the Minister and the NFU, with the CLA tagging along behind, became a regular, almost a weekly, event. So began the way our farmers submitted to state control. More strictly, it was corporativist control, for the public, whether as taxpayers or consumers, had little influence over their deliberations. According to corporativist philosophy, just two should decide what ought to be done: the government and 'the industry'. Considering how soon after the 1939–1945 War this began, it is surprising how much the process of consultation resembled the way our erstwhile enemies had managed their own agriculture.

The Treasury occasionally demurred at the level of spending by the Minister of Agriculture, and from time to time this inhibited him from giving away to the farmers all the money he would have liked. After all, success or popularity was measured by the largesse distributed, so he had a natural interest in getting as much as he could out of the Treasury, and when he failed to do so the NFU obliged with some criticism of the Minister himself. Nothing too severe was spoken – the comfortable relationship must not be disturbed – but it was strong enough to convince the rank and file farmer that the NFU was fighting his case, and strong enough also to enable the Minister to tell the Treasury that the farmer's anger had to be abated. A game was being played; not quite collusion, but each side knew the other's difficulties as well as their own, and both found it served their purpose to be accommodating. So when the Minister of the day called for more food to be grown, an echo came from the NFU.

On the touchline has been another interest, the agrochemical industry. One day the political activities of this industry will come under closer scrutiny and the story will be told of the influence it has wielded. There is no money to be made out of low-geared farming; but the more highly geared it becomes, the more the industry can sell. Its sales to farmers were but a few millions of £s in 1946. In 1982, the value of such sales by ICI alone was no less than £1,350 millions. ICI admits this is its most profitable branch of activity and it has become its largest. It has invested hundreds of millions of pounds of capital in developing its agricultural interest.

One charge can be proved against it: it has found it worthwhile to spend a small proportion of this money in promoting the present agricultural policy. At a very early stage it saw the potential of the Common Agricultural Policy, and the ICI boardroom became the scene of the first fund raising for the European Movement. It set up a department for the specific purpose of influencing MPs and Civil Servants. The head of the department shared an eccentricity with me – we were members of both the Carlton and the Reform Clubs. Our motives, I hope, were different. He set himself up as an excellent host; he knew a good wine, as the saying goes, and an invitation from him was a promise of generous hospitality. The frequency with which he entertained civil servants at the Reform Club was well known. It gave the observing cynics plenty to speculate about.

In the 1970s he was particularly active. The late Mr Asher Winegarten, Director General of the NFU, was also a member of the Reform Club at that time, so too was Sir Freddy Kearns, the Permanent Secretary to the Ministry of Agriculture, and later recruited by the NFU to be its consultant. Several others of considerable influence in agricultural policy were also to be found regularly in the Reform Club. The irony of it! As they stood to drink their gin and tonics before lunch, they were but a few feet away from a portrait of C.P. Villiers, the MP for Wolverhampton for sixty years who long before Cobden and Bright came to the fore was the lonely campaigner against the Corn Laws and who proposed a motion in the House every year against agricultural protectionism. When by themselves, they would eat together in a room set aside for members, the very room where the Cobden Club was founded to resist a return to the Corn Laws. Then after lunch, they would climb the stairs to drink their cups of coffee and glasses of port in the gallery – beneath two portraits that adorn its walls. They are of Richard Cobden and John Bright, no less.

Contacts at high level were of inestimable value to the agro-chemical industry. To watch one of their 'government affairs officers' enter a party where the farming establishment was present was enough to open one's eyes to the regard it had for him and the influence he wielded. The warmest shake of hand – even an embrace or two – genial smiles, followed by close attention to what he said. As he went about the room, heads would turn and in each knot he joined, he became its centre. A stranger to the scene would have assumed he was the most important man there in British agriculture.

The clearing banks and the larger merchant banks, which have been lending money to agriculture on an increasing scale, have also spent large sums on advertising to the British people the advantages of the Common Market, especially the Common Agricultural Policy; and those who have lent the most have spent the most. One of them was particularly keen to persuade us of the benefits of the Common Market, in all its aspects, at the time of the Referendum. That it had invested more money in agriculture than the others may have been a mere coincidence; but I have before me some of the material put out by this famous high street bank: some of the arguments are pitched at an uncommonly high note, and the facts recited could not have stemmed from the thorough research that banks usually insist upon.

This bank, certainly in my constituency, and I believe elsewhere, was freely lending money to landowners, but it was being quite unreasonable with businessmen anxious to expand their enterprises and to employ more people, even though the sums of money they asked for were paltry compared with what the bank might give a landowner in order to buy up another farm. (The latter almost invariably caused more farm workers to lose their jobs.)

The relationship between the NFU and the Ministry has grown closer and more comfortable in the years I have been an MP. In 1966, when I was first elected, their lobbyists were frequently in and around the precincts of the House, inveigling MPs to pursue one matter or another, drinking in the Strangers' Bar, inviting MPs to lunch with them and issuing invitations to dine at Agriculture House with various leaders of the NFU.

Now every lobbyist knows one trick of the trade: if you know you are going to be successful in representations made through ordinary channels in the Ministry, there is no point in spending time and money organising MPs. It is therefore of some significance that in recent years, certainly from 1979 to 1983, the NFU lobbyists have hardly bothered MPs at all. The very fact that nowadays they do not trouble much to be around Westminster shows their confidence in their own power and influence. It is a curious thought, at a time when anyone who can see what is coming knows that drastic change is unavoidable. It will not be long now before even the most dedicated believer in the present system will be forced to realise that the party is over.

2/Isn't the Farmer a Businessman?

One of the reasons why agriculture has taken a wrong turning is that there has been no clear idea whether the farmer should be treated as a businessman or as a kind of public servant. Because no policy maker has tried to answer that question there has been a lot of muddled thinking which has taken farming up into the clouds. Yet the question is crucial: it should be the starting point in any discussion about a change of policy.

Now if we decide the farmer is a businessman, a whole series of other questions get answered quite easily. A businessman is there to look after himself; his business is his affair; whether it flourishes or fails is primarily his concern and to a somewhat lesser extent the concern of his employees, his creditors and professional advisers. It follows that the essence of a businessman is that he gets his income from his customers, and his business comes to an end if his customers do not like the price, the quality or anything else about what he has for sale. As a general rule, the government does not support him with money taken away from other businessmen. Put in the same category, the farmer would be deemed just one more man in the chain of businessmen that brings our food to our table.

He may happen to grow what we eat, but is he any more important than the others in the chain? Tractors have been an indispensible part of the farm for a long time, so the man in Coventry who designs or helps to make them cannot be dismissed as of no consequence, nor the men who drill for the oil the tractor uses. The farm of half a century ago might have been well-nigh self-sufficient, except for the blacksmith in the village and the seed merchant in the market town. Today, the farmer needs the supplies of a whole range of businessmen before he can begin a single day's work. The great chemical companies will send him not one but perhaps a dozen different sorts of herbicide, pesticide and fungicide, and the great fertiliser companies will send him a variety of different artificial fertilisers. Oil companies, machinery distributors, transport companies, seed merchants and others will also be at his service. Every one of them is a business, being run for a profit like any other commercial concern; and all of them depend upon other businesses to enable them to supply or service the farmer. In modern agriculture, they are all essential links in the chain that brings our food to us.

Once the farmer has done his job, and whatever he produces passes out of the farm gate, another series of people become no less essential before the food is on our table. Road haulage contractors, corn merchants, slaughterers, dairymen, all sorts of food processors, canners and freezers, must play a part. Again, every one of them is engaged in a straightforward commercial activity; they are businessmen, plain and simple.

So the modern farmer finds himself as one link in a chain of perhaps a hundred different businesses all involved in some degree in the business of feeding the nation. Without those other businesses the farmer could not provide us with an ounce of food, yet he himself is no longer regarded as a businessman whose income should come from his customers.

Nor does he wish to be treated as one. At least, that is the official view of the National Farmers' Union, though disquiet is growing among farmers who have had time to reflect upon the dangerous consequences that will follow if the present policy continues. In the short term, a large number of them have gained, but the gain can only be sustained by ever higher levels of price support. How can policy makers now justify still more taxpayers' money being given to expand production when demand is standing still? The dilemma is made the more serious when the farmer realises that the cost of everything he needs to buy for his farm will go on increasing, and those higher costs can only be met by higher farmgate prices. His grandfather – that much derided figure with a 'dog and stick' – had his worries, but not that one. It enabled him to survive. The dog and the stick were simply got; no sales representative from a great chemical company called to take orders for them, and no overdraft was needed to pay for them. Tomorrow's survivors will be the men who can keep costs down when farmgate prices cease to rise; but the ruthless pressures placed upon everyone who farms today make that task supremely difficult.

One way out of the dilemma is to take away any pretext that the farmer is a businessman and make him a public servant. Unable to balance the books, he would, quite simply, have to be taken over by some agency of the government. That, of course, is the socialist solution, and it is not only in the Labour Party that the idea has its supporters. I know one Socialist who is content with the present policy, despite its social injustices, because he is certain it will end in the land being nationalised and farming collectivised.

The NFU wants a farmer to have the advantages of being both a businessman and a public servant, without the disadvantages of either. He should have all the independence and dignity that goes with standing on his own feet, with the comfort of a sofa to rest upon should life prove difficult. The taxpayer who pays the bills for him can still be ordered off the land as a common trespasser. So far no very cogent reason has been advanced why this one man of the many who find us our food should have it both ways. Why not the corn merchant, the seed salesman or the slaughterer as well? They also share in the ups and downs of harvests, the cycles and oddities of uncertain demand.

The sooner the farmer decides which he would rather be, businessman or public servant, the better. Trying to make him one half a public servant puts him in a peril he does not deserve, for once the public grasp the relationship, he will have upon him another set of pressures besides those imposed upon him by the many commercial and banking concerns that govern much of his life today.

Those who are worried about the changing face of our landscape, the welfare of farm animals and the way our soil is drugged with ever larger doses of poison will be horrified at the idea of farmers becoming businessmen, unfettered by political control. I hope I can reassure them. The political controls that I object to are the ones that flow from a price support policy. Because this policy has had the opposite effect of what was intended, farmers are driven to the very deeds the conservationists, welfarists and ecologists disapprove of. Their objectives, which are shared by more farmers than they may realise, will be obtained if, firstly, the present policy is brought to an end and, secondly, farmers are subject to the law of the land like any other businessmen.

The destruction of our countryside can be stopped by applying planning restrictions on agriculture similar to those imposed upon businessmen. Two new buildings may look identical to the passer by: one will need planning permission, but not the other. If I put five parrots in a cage that should hold only one, I will be prosecuted; but not if I put five hens in it. I can pollute the atmosphere as a farmer, but not as a businessman. My friends in the Thames Water Authority tell me that they commit an offence if they ask an employee to take a hook to trim the sides of our river by himself, but I, as a farmer, can ask Billy who works for me to do exactly the same job and I am innocent of the crime.

Quite a few new laws need to be passed to bring to an end some of the undesirable practices of modern farming. Let them be passed; but some of them will not be necessary, once we have removed the root cause. Many of our present laws and much of our public money positively encourage the owners and occupiers of agricultural land to make changes that are disagreeable to the rest of us. Thatched barns get pulled down and replaced by concrete monstrosities; rivers are dredged and the trees on the bank cut down; stone walls are taken away; many thousands of miles of hedges and many thousands of acres of woodland succumb to the bulldozer. And in the uplands, either vast areas of dreary conifers blanket the hillside or great stretches of beautiful high country, where the public once freely walked or rode, have miles of barbed wire and sheep fencing, serving both to keep out the public and convert at high cost our worst quality land into third rate pasture.

The alternative is to encourage owners and occupiers of such land to keep it looking agreeable to the rest of us. If there are social and economic reasons why the public should be taxed to induce a minority to go on living in the more isolated and beautiful parts of our country, there is a better way than subsidising them to grow ultra-expensive food. Some of these quite ordinary farmers in the mountains of Wales and the hills of Scotland are costing us about £50,000 a year each to support. Larger farmers are costing us much more: one known to me has an income of about £10,000, but the taxpayer, in one way or another, is paying out £75,000 a year for him.

It would be much cheaper for the taxpayer and more beneficial to the owners and occupiers of this kind of land, quite apart from the environmental advantages, if a system of landscape amenity grants were to be given. The Field Monument Act 1972 established a precedent, and the idea was taken several stages further by the Wildlife and Countryside Act 1981. The first step would be to treat the farmer like any other businessman in the matter of planning control. Just as a businessman or anyone else must apply to the local authority for permission to change the use of his property, so should the farmer. It would be to the farmer's advantage to do so because if permission were refused, a grant would be given to compensate him for the loss of income caused by the refusal, and also to maintain whatever it was he wanted to remove. The thatched barn would then survive and be looked after, instead of gradually falling down as all but a few of them are. The hedges and woodlands would live on, and so would our wetlands and all the thousands of places that make up the diminishing habitat of our wild life. I have discussed this idea with many a farmer: I have yet to find one who disagrees with me. After all, it is their countryside too; many of them have known it since their childhood, and have good reason to be more fond of it than any visitor who passes by.

Who should administer the scheme is a subordinate detail. Not many planning officers employed by District Councils have much imagination; chivvying the hapless householder on minutiae is rather their forte; and the planning officers employed by County Councils tend to be concerned with strategic issues. Perhaps the Ministry of Agriculture, once its officials imbibed the new philosophy, or the Countryside Commission or the Nature Conservancy Council; but choosing the most suitable body need cause no great anxiety.

Nor should the principles to be applied occasion any difficulty. Agricultural valuers spend already part of their time in negotiating compensation with public authorities when they require changes to be made affecting the use of agricultural land. The terms of wayleaves for the gas and electricity industries are an example. There is also a valuation to be made when the County Council wants to take farmland to widen a road. When the parties fail to agree, there is recourse to the Lands Tribunal. A great fund of knowledge and experience is already available on the subject; to extend it further would be a simple task.

The principle of these landscape amenity grants – or whatever other term for the idea is adopted – reinforces the status of the farmer as a businessman. The public is made to recognise that he is running a business which must pay its way and give him the livelihood that is due to him. He, in turn, is assured of his independence and self respect. He is not paid money by a resentful taxpayer to produce food in a hopelessly inefficient manner; he earns his money in the market place because he is efficient and because his customer acknowledges it. Between the farmer, the landowner, the taxpayer and the consumer a common interest would emerge, and goodwill rather than resentment prevail.

Ought the principle to be extended to the welfare of farm animals? A grant to keep cows, pigs and poultry in conditions that allow them to move around and breath fresh air, instead of spending their lives in stalls or cages, would have the approval of many people. In a subsequent chapter I try to show that the undesirable extremes of intensive husbandry would come to an end naturally were we to change the present agricultural policy. That judgment may, of course, be over-optimistic; but surely the answer is to change the policy first, make some of the practices illegal (for example, keeping a sow locked inside a stall unable to turn round for four months at a time is indefensible, as every right minded stockman agrees) and then see how the changes in animal husbandry develop?

What is absolutely certain is that the present high-input/high-output policy is going to drive farmers into keeping their animals more intensively, and that means breeding animals that can only thrive in such conditions. More antibiotics will have to be administered to them – and passed into the meat and eggs for us to eat – and still more public money spent on research to devise ever more intensive methods. Visiting the animal research establishment at Babraham is enough to convince anyone that this research has no limit: there I saw the udders of goats transplanted onto their necks to see whether they would produce more milk that way! The average size of the herds and flocks will under the present system continue to get bigger, the smaller producers will continue to disappear, and livestock farming will become ever more an industry in the control of a handful of major companies. All of that adds up to another reason why the farmer should demur at the road he is being driven along.

In the chapter 'The Poor Consumer', a glance is taken at the evidence to support the charge that some of our modern farming practices are having a questionable effect upon the nation's health. Perhaps not enough is known to decide whether the time has come for a system of grants to be given to farmers to encourage them to abandon at least some of them, but in an ideal world it would be possible to prevent certain herbicides being used. An international convention under the auspices of the Food and Agricultural Organisation could agree to their use coming to an end, then each country could pass the legislation necessary to prohibit them. Until that comes about, there is no reason why we should not impose our own prohibition and also put an embargo upon imports from those countries that continue to use them. In the case of a commodity that we have to import in large quantities, it might be necessary to give our own producers grants to enable them to put onto the market the additional supplies we needed. A subsidy to safeguard the health of the taxpaying public might be looked upon more favourably than the present system that effectively does the opposite.

Now let us look at the alternative – the farmer as a public servant. The vision of security throughout a working life and a pension at sixty may sooth the eyes of anyone working long hours in the heat of a summer's harvest or in the bitter winds of a February lambing. The worry of the overdraft climbing upwards disappears and the old question of whether to get bigger or get out does not have to be answered. It has its attractions. It is like working for the Ministry's advisory service, ADAS; and just as students emerging from agricultural college do not queue up to join ADAS, but seek the challenge and exhilaration of farming on their own account, doing it their way and no one else's, so it seems the temperament of most of our farmers would militate against this new form of public service. That the successful farmers are answerable to no one except themselves is one reason why this alternative is unlikely to be sought by many of them.

Yet it could be forced upon them. What will happen if a government of the left takes office, and pulls the rug from under their feet? The longer the policy goes on, the more the farmer becomes dependent upon the taxpayer. When it began after the War, price support from the taxpayer provided the farmer with about 25 to 35 per cent of his income. Gradually the percentage crept up, until it averaged about 60 per cent. Since the Common Agricultural Policy has applied, the percentage has risen to extraordinary heights. For the year 1977-78, 82 per cent of farmers' income came from the taxpayer; in the next year it rose to 105 per cent, that is to say, for every £100 the farmer received as income, the cost to the taxpayer was £5 more. In 1980-81, it was 166 per cent. Last year it was over 200 per cent!

We can arrive at that figure by quite a simple process. The 1984 *Annual Review* has estimated farmers' income as totalling £1,536 millions. At the time of the General Election, Mr Peter Walker, while still Minister for Agriculture, admitted to readers of the *British Farmer and Stockbreeder* that if we were to go over to deficiency payments, the cost to the taxpayer of maintaining farm income at the present level would be £3,000 millions. This sum therefore represents the amount that the farmer is now getting through artificially high prices. The other price support to the farmer came more directly from the public in the form of grants and subsidies, and for that year, £1,356 millions were given. However, £1,015 millions were refunded by Brussels out of the funds that accrue from the taxation the EEC imposes, so that the net figure was £341 millions, to be added to the £3,000 millions. Hence the total is over twice as much as farmers' incomes.

The percentage figures point upwards. They must. The more food we produce, the greater the surpluses, and the more of these we export, the higher the burden of the export subsidies. The other reason why the percentage increases is that the further we push ourselves towards self-sufficiency the higher the cost of support. At some time in the future a halt will have to be called. The amount of money given in price support will then be cut or stopped altogether. The former may seem more probable than the latter; but once it is understood that price support does not, in fact, support farmers, the whole system could come to an end and be replaced by something else.

Public opinion, however, will play its part in deciding what the new policy will be. By then the British people may have digested the fact that the total amount of money they have given to farmers to support their incomes (already £62,000 millions in current terms!) is nearly the value of all our agricultural land. The moral argument for its public ownership will appear much stronger than any of us concerned with agriculture might wish. Farmers will not be able to carry on with the high-cost methods of husbandry that the system has driven them to adopt; they will turn to the Government for assistance, and it will be given on the basis of farmers becoming public servants. Public ownership of land, in one form or another, might follow, but an extensive system of state control would be almost inevitable. Some agency of the government would decree what kinds of food would be produced on each farm – probably by quotas – and marketing would be ordered and disciplined. Strict control over land use would have to follow, lest the occupier started to produce for the black market. Even the possibility of being driven towards that end by our existing policy ought to make everyone connected with agriculture pause a while and consider the consequences of what we are doing.

The NFU leaders repeat again and again that criticisms of our present policy are 'farmer bashing'. It shows they do not understand what the criticism is about: it is about the policy that has been imposed upon agriculture. The policy has been decided by politicians, and while it is true that the leaders of the NFU have gone along with it, that is far from saying that farmers generally have taken part in creating it. The NFU is effectively controlled by large-scale farmers, overwhelmingly interested in the arable sector, and they are the kind who can afford to employ managers and foremen who have the day-to-day charge of the farm while they themselves are away in London. Very few members of the NFU Council have farms of the average size, let alone small farms. As one of them said to me once, 'You have to have 750 acres to be farming nowadays.' (The average sized farm in England and Wales is 127 acres.)

I have likened modern farming to Concorde. Two or three times a week it flies over our house, going the length of the Pang Valley on its way to New York; and when it gains height through a darkening sky, the resemblance is even greater. Both are a triumph of technology, both economically a disaster, and soon both will be enveloped in the threatening clouds.

There is another point of resemblance. No one blames the crew of Concorde when we hear of the terrible cost of keeping it in the air. The crew's job is to fly the aircraft given to them. So it is with agriculture. Farmers must work the system given to them. Unless they happen to be millionaire dilettantes, they have no choice in the matter. No one should blame tens of thousands of farmers who are cultivating their land and rearing their stock in the way the policy makers bid them to do. In so far as he is still a businessman and not a public servant, anyone engaged in agriculture must respond to the signals of the market place. What has gone wrong is that the politicians have taken over the signalling system and reduced it to a state of chaotic disorder. Wrong signals have been sent out because only the customer who wants to eat some food can send out an accurate message about the particular kind of food he happens to want. The Minister of Agriculture in London and the EEC Commissioner of Agriculture in Brussels are both very clever and conscientious men, but neither they nor any of the thousands of officials who advise them are qualified to manage something so delicate and complicated as the food market.

If we lived in special isolation from the rest of the world and set up a rigidly controlled economy, with ration cards for everyone and the death sentence for every black marketeer, our Minister of Agriculture might, given a battery of computers, lots of data and a little bit of luck, decide how many refrigerators and deep freezes a nation of fifty-five million might buy in the forthcoming year. To go further and decide what items of food would go into them in twelve months time would simply be far beyond the realm of possibility. Not even in the most dirigiste economy can that be done. A totalitarian minister can control the manufacture and sale of mechanical things – like refrigerators and deep freezes – but the growing and marketing of food depends upon elements beyond human control. It is quite astonishing that such a simple truth is not understood and the consequences of it acted upon. But I suspect the truth is understood; unfortunately, it is rather enjoyable taking over the powers of the signalling system. All Ministers enjoy power; some enjoy it too much, and those are the ones who cause the most trouble.

The consumer and the farmer, the buyer and the seller, can between them, if left alone by the politicians, get British agriculture into the right input/output ratio. The ratio will be lower than it is today, but even if we wanted to go into lowest-gear farming, it would now be technically and physically impossible. We need something between Peter Walker's top gear and the ecologists' lowest. Of course, the latter may seem desirable and perhaps we might be able to go back to it in another generation or two, but until then it is a pipe dream. Let us aim for what is practicable. In the meantime, the consumer and the farmer should be allowed to come closer together. The real answer to the Green Movement is, I believe, to root out the cause of the damage instead of trying to rub out its effects. The cause is misguided political control.

In the following chapters I have selected five areas of shame and five groups of victims. They are human victims and, if the logic is valid, they add up to many, many hundreds of thousands of people. They are the ones who lose by the present policy; those who gain are, comparatively speaking, a handful. I have left out three areas, because they have been explored already by others and by three women writers in particular. Ruth Harrison wrote *Animal Machines*; Rachel Carson, *Silent Spring* and Marion Shoard, *The Theft of the Countryside*. Notable books indeed, but as every month goes by, each of them becomes more out of date. The pace of change is quickening. Animal machines have become more mechanical, spring has become more silent and more of the countryside has been stolen. Yes, even since 1980 when the last of those books was written, there have been thousands of irreversible changes wrought upon our landscape.

By placing myself beside them, no doubt I shall be accused yet again of 'farmer bashing'. How often has the NFU said that if the housewife wants cheap food, people must accept these methods of mass production. Critics of modern farming had better keep quiet or agree to pay more for what they eat.

Of course, this shows up the NFU leaders as proper little Englanders. They would be wrong even if the only food available were produced on our own overcrowded island; but there are also vast areas beyond the oceans capable of growing all the food we could possibly consume. Hundreds of thousands of farmers would like to send us that food at a cheaper price than we now pay, and the housewife would like to buy it – for precisely the same reason as the farmer likes to buy cheaper tractors made abroad rather than in Coventry. The housewife would pay less for her bread, butter, beef, lamb and sugar if our importers were allowed to bring them into the country without paying huge levies or duties or if, in the case of sugar for example, the terms of trading were not prejudiced against the cheaper producer.

Other items of food such as pork, bacon, eggs, poultry meat and milk would be cheaper if the feeding stuffs sold to their producers were not artificially raised in price by the present policy. The fact is that high-cost farming forces the farmer to extract the most he can out of his livestock and his land. It is worse than a treadmill: work hard enough on that and one can at least keep at the same level. With the present system, the farmer must produce more and more, year after year, and some time in the future he will be unable to do so.

In every part of our rural countryside I know there are lots of people thinking about this road taken by agriculture. There must be many of them, because I have received scores and scores of worried letters on the subject. The greatest number have come from farmers themselves. Among those who have written to me they are some of the bitterest critics of the system. None has been so poignant as a small tenant farmer with a superb herd of dairy cows, each one bred and reared by himself.

Being a tenant, he cannot expand the size of his farm, but he could increase the size of his herd. In that way he would become more 'viable' – in plainer language, it means he could remain in farming for a few years more. But a larger herd would prevent him from giving his cows the care and attention he believes he owes them. He is a true husbandman and he does not want to do it. His farming is doomed.

If a policy of supporting farmers means anything at all, it means keeping them in business, and since our present policy was introduced half our farmers have gone out of business. The more we have talked about agricultural efficiency, the more we have lost efficient farmers.

3/Where's Our Money Gone?

The Table on the next page sets out how much money the British taxpayer has given to agriculture since 1955 for the purpose of supporting prices. The first column states the fiscal year; the second, the cost of price support in current terms. Those figures are meaningless in conditions of inflation, so the third column sets out the cost to the taxpayer as measured in today's terms. These figures, it must be emphasised, do not reveal the full cost of supporting agriculture. They leave out the thousands of millions of pounds of other money given to agriculture in the way of subsidies, production grants, advisory services and tax allowances. They relate purely to price support.

Stated in 1984 terms, the cost since 1955 comes to a total of £50,796 millions. Before 1955 the cost of food subsidies given to the consumer were subsumed in the cost of price support to the farmer. To disentangle the two with precision is not feasible, but it is reasonable to assume that the cost of price support for the previous years was broadly in line with what it was for 1955-56. The cost in current terms for that year was £206 millions and in 1984 terms, £1,696 millions.

To assume £1,500 millions for each of those years must be fair. To find the cost to the taxpayer since price support began in 1947 we therefore add £12,000 millions to our previous total to make £62,796 millions.

Divided among 220,000 farmers still in business, it comes to £285,000 for each of them. But as we saw in the previous chapter, many farmers do not receive this kind of support – indeed they are paying for it. So for those who are the beneficiaries the average must be raised still higher. (Of course, it is true that there used to be more than twice as many farmers as there are today – a fact which shows the failure of price

37

U.K. Expenditure on price support

	Cost in current prices £ millions	Cost in terms of 1983/84 prices £ millions
1955-56	206	1,696
1956-57	239	1,863
1957-58	284	2,124
1958-59	241	1,750
1959-60	257	1,846
1960-61	263	1,852
1961-62	343	2,336
1962-63	310	2,048
1963-64	295	1,903
1964-65	264	1,631
1965-66	238	1,405
1966-67	229	1,296
1967-68	261	1,436
1968-69	265	1,390
1969-70	268	1,335
1970-71	256	1,179
1971-72	411	1,731
1972-73	395	1,542
1973-74	289	1,051
1974-75	398	1,214
1975-76	703	1,706
1976-77	739	1,584
1977-78	1,061	1,999
1978-79	1,329	2,268
1979-80	1,500	2,191
1980-81	1,928	2,372
1981-82	2,500	2,799
1982-83	3,000	3,150

Notes: (a) Current costs are from the *Annual Reviews* until import levies were introduced; thereafter the costs are from the Institute of Fiscal Studies except for the two last years when they are based on estimates by the Minister of Agriculture.

(b) Costs in 1983/84 terms are derived using the implied deflator for GDP at market prices assuming a 5% increase between 1982-83 and 1983-84. (Source: CSO Database DJAF, DJCX.)

support – but in counting the cost of the system it is only sensible to divide it among those who have in fact survived with its help.)

In the last year before the system of price support began, total farm incomes were £220 millions. Since then the pound has fallen in value to less than one tenth, so farm incomes should now be over £2,200 millions to maintain their value. The 1984 *Annual Review* stated that they were £1,500 millions. The basis of the calculation has changed somewhat over the intervening years, but making every possible allowance for that there remains a considerable fall. Farm incomes are one third less now than they were before we began spending £62,796 millions to support them. If those farmers who have survived are better off it is only because half of them have *not* survived.

So where has our money gone? One explanation is that it has been lost in the sheer state of inefficiency of modern agriculture. Farmers are goaded into producing at high cost a great deal of food which cannot be sold at an economic price because the customer has not enough money to pay for it. Obviously there is some truth in that for the pattern of food consumption has changed remarkably, as the later chapter on 'The Poor Consumer' points out. Yet that cannot be the complete explanation when the price support is now in the form of import levies which are passed on to the consumer to pay. We must look elsewhere.

As farmers have not had their incomes raised, this vast sum of money must have gone in some other direction. One clue came to me when I discussed with my constituents their difficulties. The tenant farmer with less than sixty acres – of whom there used to be many fifteen years ago – seems to be in a markedly different position to an owner-occupier with the same size and type of farm. Agricultural rents have been going up very steeply and the very rich land in my constituency can fetch over £100 an acre. The owner-occupier, once he has paid off his mortgage, finds himself placed quite differently, his asset steadily rising in value. The gap between the two grows wider each year, so could it be that this money given by the taxpayer has gone into inflating land values?

I decided to compile a table to show how the value of

agricultural land has risen, over and above the rate of inflation. To obtain an accurate picture, I divided the land into its five Grades, then with advice from agricultural valuers who practised before the War I put down the average value of each Grade in 1939. As the pound has fallen to one fifteenth of its value then, I multiplied that estimate by 15, so the second column states what the value of our agricultural land would be if it had risen according to the rate of inflation since 1939. (I took 1939, rather than 1946, as the base year since there were obvious distortions of the price mechanism during the war.) Next, with the aid of valuers now practising, I calculated the actual value today. The last column in the table is the 'excess value per acre'. This is the difference between the actual value of our farmland and the 1939 value when brought up to 1984 terms.

	Acres	1939 value per acre x 15	Actual value per acre	Excess value per acre
Grade I	1,263,628	£750	£3,500	£2,750
Grade II	6,588,921	£600	£3,000	£2,400
Grade III	22,068,374	£405	£1,800	£1,395
Grade IV	8,890,531	£150	£1,200	£1,050
Grade V	6,318,144	£ 75	£ 900	£ 825

Now let us calculate the excess value of each Grade by multiplying the excess value of each acre by the number of acres in each Grade. The following is the result:

Grade I	£ 3,473,250,000
Grade II	£15,811,200,000
Grade III	£30,784,860,000
Grade IV	£ 9,334,500,000
Grade V	£ 5,212,350,000

Adding up those five together we reach a total of £64,516,160,000. Well now, is it a coincidence? People with money to invest will look for places to put it where the return is highest. If a government is foolish enough to spend taxpayers' money to raise the return on one kind of asset rather than another, it is natural for the investor to take advantage of the folly by investing in that kind of asset. Lest it is not self-evident, more is said about it in the chapter 'Two Million Unemployed'.

The Victims

4/The Efficient Farmer

A major victim of the present agricultural policy is the efficient farmer. Already it has forced many thousands of them off the land. They are to be found as lorry drivers, milk roundsmen, in the hotel trade, in journalism, but mostly far removed from what they used to do well. Those who remain are among the ones having greatest difficulty in holding on to their farms. Such a sweeping assertion, contradicting so bluntly the combined wisdom of the Ministry of Agriculture, the National Farmers Union, spokesmen for the agrochemical industry and most writers on agricultural matters, demands substantial evidence to support it. Much of this book will be about that evidence. Subsequent chapters will look at what has happened to efficient farmers in other parts of the world and how many of them have become the poorer for what we have done. This chapter is about the efficient farmer in our own country, and why he has also become a casualty of the system.

Efficiency is a word often on the lips of the farming establishment. When pressed to explain what is meant, they talk about productivity. Now productivity is about the relationship of labour and output, the business of getting fewer people to produce as much as before. An increase in productivity means reducing the number of people to do the same job. Even at a time of large-scale unemployment, it is deemed to be desirable in itself and a measure of increased efficiency. The figures for agriculture are, indeed, impressive, and they are set out on the next page.

British agriculture has lost no less than two thirds of its labour force in the period of price support. Furthermore, these figures are for all farm workers, male and female, full-time, seasonal and casual. If only full-time farm workers are considered, the fall has been still greater; and in the last twelve

Year	Total Number of Farmworkers
1946	976,000
1947	980,000
1948	932,000
1949	934,000
1950	918,000
1951	882,000
1952	869,000
1953	842,000
1954	815,000
1955	788,000
1956	754,000
1957	750,000
1958	730,000
1959	719,000
1960	693,000
1961	662,000
1962	633,000
1963	611,000
1964	584,000
1965	551,000
1966	522,000
1967	485,000
1968	450,000
1969	433,000
1970	425,000
1971	418,000
1972	413,000
1973	416,000
1974	398,000
1975	
1976	383,000
1977	379,000
1978	374,000
1979	358,000
1980	353,000
1981	342,000
1982	338,000

years, since we went over to import levies with the emphasis on arable farming instead of livestock production, their decline has been at an even faster rate, from 250,000 to 167,000.

At the same time, agricultural output has risen considerably. Gross output in 1970-71 was £2,644 millions; for 1983 it is estimated at £11,595 millions. That is nearly a five-fold increase, and, on the face of it, most impressive. It looks too good to be true. It is too good to be true, because it does not take account of inflation and also because output figures are meaningless unless one takes into account inputs; and the cost of the inputs has gone up at a faster rate than the value of the outputs. It is one more commentary on why agriculture has taken a wrong turning. Anyone can increase output to a dazzling height, provided he pays no heed to inputs. To gauge the true value of what any branch of our economy has achieved, we must subtract the cost of inputs from the value of the outputs, then subtract depreciation of plant, machinery and buildings. Having done so, we arrive at the net product.

Fortunately, the *Annual Review of Agriculture* does these sums for us. It defines net product as 'a measure of the value added by the agricultural industry to all the goods and services purchased from outside agriculture after provision has been made for depreciation'. The *Review* takes 1980 as the base year, giving the net product for that year the index of 100; and it goes back to 1970 – very conveniently for us, for that was a full year before the import levies began. Allowing for inflation, the index for 1970 is 119. This means, of course, that British agriculture's net product was substantially more in 1970 than it was in 1980. 1980 is the lowest point in the years 1970-1983 and net product is forecast to rise to 104 for last year, but it is still well below what it was in 1970.

What about improvements in productivity, though? Let us see what has happened on one particular farm, say one of four hundred acres. Back in 1946 its owner or tenant would have been fully engaged in managing it and four men would have been employed. Today it would be one man. Where have the other three gone? One is a lorry driver employed by a firm of agricultural merchants, founded since 1946 to supply local farmers with fertilisers, herbicides and such like. Another has left the district, unable to find other employment, and is now living in the Midlands making agricultural machinery of a kind that was not invented in 1946. The third may have joined the pool of permanently unemployed or perhaps he has been recruited by one of the companies who specialise in putting up new buildings for farmers, or possibly one of the firms of agricultural contractors who are expert at draining and other well-subsidised land improvement schemes.

Fewer people are engaged on the farm itself all the year round, but many more are engaged in supplying or servicing agriculture. The NFU admits in its publicity leaflets that agriculture employs indirectly hundreds of thousands of men and women. Thus there has been a transfer from one sphere to another; and it is questionable whether the total number of people employed in and for agriculture has become less than it was in 1946.

Agriculture's productivity is based upon a fallacy. A few generations ago, a farm was virtually self sufficient. The carthorse was the main source of power; he was bred on the farm or in the neighbourhood by another farmer. His source of energy was hay and oats, both produced from the acres he spent his life upon. Such machinery as existed on the farm was simple and made in the neighbourhood or on the farm itself, for the larger farm had its own smithy. Muck from the farmyard fertilised the land, home grown barley and beans fed the stock.

Even in 1946, many of our farms were still being run on not very different principles, especially the ones in the remoter parts of the country. Up in the North, they used to speak of a 'statesman' – a farmer with his own freehold, living in independent state, buying in very little of anything, being an island to himself and his family. There is no farm like that now. The carthorse has long since left, and the tractor made in the Midlands or, as likely, somewhere abroad has taken his place. A quantity of advanced machinery is there; bag upon bag of artificial fertiliser is piled up in the barn; cannisters of herbicides stand ready for use; a hundred operations may still be performed on the same farm; but there is not a single one among them that can be undertaken without some outside help or the supply of something from off the farm.

So when we claim that productivity has increased in agriculture since, say, 1946, we are not comparing like with like. The figures that are quoted ('One man on the farm now produces enough food for 42 people,' for example) are specious and they lead to false conclusions. We must stop treating agriculture as the only part of food production. What we should be asking ourselves is how many people were engaged in the whole business of food production in any base year and comparing that number with today's. Whatever base year is selected, it is unlikely there will be sufficient difference to support the argument of productivity.

Sometimes productivity is related to acreage instead of labour, a higher yield from an acre being made the touchstone. Again the record in Britain is impressive and a triumph for applied technology. More tons of wheat grown to the acre – and many have doubled their yields – or more cows kept on the same field may seem to be worthwhile achievements, but again, is this a test of efficiency?

The fact is that those high yields have been achieved by uneconomic means. The big machines that have replaced farm labour have been written off one hundred per cent against tax for the year; the fertilisers and toxic chemicals that are poured onto the land have side effects that other people pay for; the stripping of the landscape to prepare it for this type of cultivation has been heavily subsidised. High yields do not indicate efficiency if producing them costs more than the food is worth.

In the United States and Canada, where the kind of land costing £2,000 an acre over here can be bought for £350, the farmer is under no such pressure. He can make his farm pay by growing wheat at half the yields – 1½ tons to the acre compared with the 3 tons of his English counterpart. Does the comparison make him half as efficient, or does it show to what lengths British agriculture has been driven by (among other things) the crazy over-valuation of our land that we looked at in the last chapter? Reflect that the £64,000 millions of that over-valuation represents more than £1,000 an acre: a farm of five hundred acres has to employ over half a million pounds of unjustified capital.

I would define the efficient farmer in quite simple terms. He is the man who can make a livelihood out of his farm without asking the taxpayer to subsidise him. It is a yardstick which provides a scale of efficiency: the very efficient will be running a very profitable enterprise, but even the less efficient will lead an independent life, able both to give his customers at least some degree of satisfaction and to support himself and his family. The usefulness of such farmers is self-evident, yet they are the very kind of farmer the system now liquidates. That is a strong word to use, but we will see whether it is deserved.

One of the reasons why the farming establishment disapproves of that definition of efficiency is that it claims that every country supports its agriculture. That is one of the many glib statements about agricultural policy that falls down when looked at more closely. There are (I believe) 159 self-governing countries and it may be true that they have as many different agricultural policies. What is certainly true is that about two thirds of them are developing countries, so called because their economies are still founded upon primary industries, above all agriculture. They do not have a great body of taxpayers engaged in other pursuits enabling them to subsidise farmers. Because their country's wealth springs from agriculture, the government must look to the farmers to provide revenue, not to absorb it. True, the government may give some form of assistance in the form of tariff protection or loans at a low rate of interest, but generally such help is of small significance. Tariffs have the effect of making food more expensive, and soft loans to agriculture are undesirable for a government trying to promote other industries. When closely examined, the element of subsidy given to a farmer in most countries in the Third World is an illusion.

More substantial is the argument that the rich countries support their agricultural interests. It must be conceded that all of them do so, but what must be challenged is the claim that any of them do so as much as the EEC. Norway and Switzerland come near to us, but neither they nor any other country in the world has set up such a vast range of aids and devices to distort the ordinary market forces on food. It is something of an irony. The Treaty of Rome upholds not only the freedom of trade, but

47

every other principle of a market economy. Nearly three decades on, the only common policy of consequence that is effectively in force contradicts all the fine words in the Treaty's preamble. Agriculture in the OECD countries outside the EEC tends to rely either upon tariffs for protection or some sort of price support policy, but not both. The EEC quite determinedly has adopted both forms of support, belt as well as braces. On top of them has been created an edifice embracing, in one or more of the member states, every kind of crutch and buttress found beyond the Community.

Liquidation of the efficient farmer has been a gradual process. To say how many farmers there were before the War is not easy as no official figures were obtained except when the decadal Census was taken in 1931. At that time 1,352,000 men and women described themselves as wholly engaged in agriculture and fishing; in 1951, there were 1,173,000 so engaged. To these must be added a very large number of part-time farmers. It is generally agreed that there were, in round figures, some 500,000 agricultural holdings of one kind or another and about 900,000 farm workers. There is no firm evidence of a substantial decline in the number of people on the land during the inter-War years. The decline has taken place since 1946, that is, as soon as the system of price support began, and it has continued remorselessly from then until today. Nor does any arrest in the decline appear likely. Three, four or five thousand farmers leave every year without being replaced.

This brings us to another myth to be dispelled. Almost any arable farmer would swear that he would be ruined without a system of price support. The years before the War were disastrous for him; they were black years, years of ruin and bankruptcy, years when it was impossible to earn a living by growing wheat. Yet what the record shows is that, on average, and in real terms, wheat prices were higher than they are today. It is true that the price used to vary considerably from harvest to harvest, but let us look at all the years between the repeal of the Corn Protection Act in 1921 and the passing of the Wheat Act in 1932, the years when there was no support for wheat growers. *Agricultural Records AD 220-1977*, a fascinating book edited by Ralph Whitlock, gives us the prices.

Year	Price of wheat per hundredweight		
	£	s	d
1922		11	2
1923		9	10
1924		11	6
1925		12	2
1926		12	5
1927		11	6
1928		10	0
1929		9	10
1930		8	0
1931		5	9

The average for those ten years works out at about 10s 2½d a hundredweight or £10.4s.4d a ton. Though the rate of inflation varied slightly throughout those ten years, to multiply that average by 15 would translate quite closely into today's value. It means that throughout that decade the average price the arable farmer received for his wheat was in today's money £153. That is higher than the price any farmer has received for his wheat in recent years and compares with a price of £110 that he is likely to receive this season. Life may have been hard in the years before the War – but not because of free trade.

If wheat prices were so much higher in those black years, how can it be that every arable farmer in the land has convinced himself that he is better off now? The answer is that he is, in fact, better off – but not because of the system of price support. Price support has not given him the new varieties of seed and the new technology of fertilisation and cultivation. The seventeen or eighteen hundredweight of wheat grown before the War was on good land, Grade I and II, and on this land today three or four tons are grown. It is the fourfold increase in yields that has caused the arable farmer to prosper. It is the technologist, not the politician, who has been his friend.

The inter-war period was a time when British agriculture was expanding, and compared with other trades and industries it was doing surprisingly well. Mass unemployment, with just over three million out of work in 1932, blighted the industrial areas; dole money of ten shillings a week and £2 or £3 for those fortunate enough to have the average wage diminished the nation's purchasing power to a pitifully low level. Inevitably, farmers were unable to prosper as they might have done; rents were not always paid, and in some areas landlords gave tenants money to look after the property until better times came. Many farmers went out of business. All that is true and anyone over the age of fifty-five – as I am – who lived in the countryside, can remember the hardship. But hardship is relative; it is futile to compare life then with what it is now; the sensible comparison must be with others in 1932. The farmer of 1932 was better off than his brother who had gone into the local town to start a business or join a profession. They were the days of the mixed farm – dairy cows, pigs, poultry, an orchard and a large vegetable garden – and its owner and his family did not go hungry, nor did the men he employed. One test of their comparative prosperity is looking at the number employed in agriculture. About three times more men and women were able to gain a livelihood out of farming than is the case today.

More sure and scientific is the evidence of the Ministry of Agriculture. Over a period of sixteen years, between 1923 and 1939, we came to have 14 per cent more cattle on our farms, 27 per cent more sheep, 45 per cent more pigs and 63 per cent more poultry. No other major industry within the United Kingdom enjoyed an expansion on that scale.

'Down corn, up horn', is an old saying. When arable prices go down, livestock returns go up. It is exactly what happened in the first thirty-nine years of this century. Mr O.J. Beilby of the Agricultural Economic Research Institute at Oxford published an index of agricultural production for that period. It included every commodity produced by our farmers, all arable crops being included along with all livestock. He made 1927-1929 the base with an index of 100. The index for 1900-1904 was the low point at 82, so that agricultural production was 18 per cent less at the turn of the century than it was in 1927-1929. It climbed up to 104 in the years 1931-1933, which means that there was a 4 per cent increase in agricultural production, notwithstanding the years of a major industrial recession and mass unemployment. It continued to climb upwards in 1934-1936 to reach the index of 110.

Mr Beilby was not alone in this research. Lord Astor and Mr Seebohm Rowntree produced an alternative index in their book *British Agriculture*. Where Mr Beilby took net output, they chose gross output, that is, they included all items produced on the farm, although they were used to produce something else, like feed barley for pigs. They decided that agricultural production rose by no less than 22 per cent in the period between 1923 and 1937.

None of this expansion was induced by quotas, subsidies, grants, tariffs, tax allowances or any of the other forms of government interference, though the passing of the Wheat Act and the introduction of the Milk Marketing Board were intended to help. The government did not believe it right to interfere with marketing or the price mechanism. It did not dictate what should be produced on our farms – the British public dictated it. As customers, they had the freedom then – which they have now lost – to decide whether to eat food from Britain or from anywhere else. And they happened to choose much of their food from Britain for the good and simple reason that it was good value for their money.

British agriculture was efficient in the sense that all the people involved were able to earn a livelihood from these farms, and not one of them was beholden to the government, politicians, civil servants, or anyone else equipped with taxpayers' money. They were truly independent; they could claim self respect and the dignity of free men. Their freedom included, of course, the freedom to buy their own needs in the cheapest market, a freedom they shared with the rest of the British people. It was the key that enabled British farmers to expand their production by some 20 per cent.

The Ministry's figures, quoted above, showed how much we increased our pig herd and poultry flocks. For generations we had fed both pigs and poultry on kitchen scraps, wheat offal and other unsaleable food found on or around the farm that would otherwise have been wasted. Both had played a minor part in the economy of the average holding, and the products of both were usually consumed by the families who owned or worked the farm, plus a few neighbours in the village who did not keep their own pigs or hens.

The supply of limitless quantities of cheap grain from North America, Argentina and Australia transformed insignificant sidelines into major branches of agriculture. Poultry farms, thousands of them, came into being. Flocks of hundreds of birds were now to be seen on the side of a south-facing hill, ranging freely, and providing the sole source of income for their owners, who in turn seemed able to engage one or two employees out of the proceeds. So, too, with pigs. Some years later I began with a herd of twenty sows and with their progeny they were enough to make a profit, after paying a man to look after them. Feeding stuffs were bought at world prices, that is, at the lowest price in the world, and so those tens of thousands of specialist livestock holdings that were springing up all over the countryside had an enormous advantage which was passed on to the consumer in the form of low-priced food. It enabled the British housewife to buy bacon, pork, ham, eggs and poultry as cheaply as any housewife in the world. As a result, demand for these particular foods increased; and the more it increased the more specialist poultry and pig farmers came into existence. Hence the figures indicating a remarkable expansion.

Incomes for all of us are far higher today and one might therefore suppose that we are still consuming as much bacon, pork, ham, eggs and poultry meat as we were in those bad old days. With the exception of poultry meat, we have witnessed a fall in consumption of all of them. There may be another reasonable explanation, but common sense suggests that we are eating less of them because our bacon, pork, ham and eggs have ceased to be the cheapest in the world; in fact, they are now among the most expensive. Poultry meat is a special case because the whole way of keeping poultry has changed out of all recognition, and economies of scale have had the effect of reducing costs. It goes without saying that poultry meat would be considerably cheaper were the producer allowed to buy his food at world prices. Feed costs are much the same from one farm to the next, though as a proportion of total costs they can vary quite materially. They tend to be for both pig and poultry men about 75 per cent of the total. If such a major item in the budget is artificially increased it must have a grave effect upon the economics of this kind of husbandry. An efficient form of farming is made uneconomic.

The example of my neighbour may serve to illustrate what has happened. For a long time, his sole income came from a herd of pigs. As each year went by he increased its size to keep pace with rising costs until 1983 when he had 350 sows. The progeny were reared for pork and as he usually got the highest price in the market, no one could easily accuse him of failing to satisfy his customers, the local butchers. The reason for the quality of his meat, he insisted, was that he fed home-mixed rations based upon maize, which he got from Bristol docks, imported from the United States. On the maize he had to pay an import levy – a tax – of nearly 100 per cent. He calculated it cost him about £30,000 a year. The burden proved too heavy: profits became losses, and eventually in 1983 he sold up. Without the levy he could have made a comfortable profit and still satisfied the local butchers with what they and their customers wanted.

That is not quite the end of the story. He owns about sixty acres of Grade III land, which for as long as I can remember has been not very good pasture. Drainage grants from the government enticed him to convert it into arable land and it now grows wheat. Of course, it is quite uneconomic as a crop, were the import levies on wheat not imposed. But now, instead of contributing £30,000 a year to the Treasury, he is taking about £15,000 a year from the taxpayer, directly or indirectly. Is he now efficient? That triumvirate of farming wisdom, the Ministry of Agriculture, the NFU and the agrochemical industry presumably would say he was.

One effect of our support policy is to make traditional animal husbandry uneconomic and to foster intensive 'factory farming'. Take pigs. A modern intensive unit of, say, three hundred sows, with the progeny going to either pork or bacon, can be established very largely with tax allowances. Anyone wanting to start a herd of the same size kept extensively – on free range – is not entitled to the same assistance. A factory farm will need only a few acres of land; these, it is true, will have to be purchased out of the owner's capital, but they are unlikely to cost more than £10,000, which represents a very small percentage of the total needed.

Next come buildings which will cost at least £100,000, and all of that can be written off against income tax over a period of seven years. Then fittings and equipment must be purchased, and these are also likely to cost more than £100,000. They include the sow stalls, a kind of iron bar cage that is large enough to contain the sow and for her to stand up and lie down, but not large enough for her to turn round: she will be kept in the stall throughout her life, apart from when she is served by the boar or when she farrows, each occasion being about twice a year. Sows used to live six or seven years, giving birth to litters large enough each time to make it worth the while of their owners to keep them for that length of time. Now sows seldom last three years: smaller, weaker litters will otherwise be born. The cost of sow stalls, farrowing pens, the automatic feeding devices and all the other factory-style equipment can be set against a single year's income tax. The advantage to a large-scale arable farmer with an income of £100,000 a year is obvious enough; the advantage to one of the many farming companies that have been formed in the last decade is still more so. It is the essential reason why this type of animal husbandry is being taken over by the companies.

They pay less tax as each year they expand, and plainly their expansion is at the expense of the small farmer. A farm, if it can be so called, where a thousand sows are kept in row after row of sow stalls has become not uncommon. Not long ago when I was invited to speak at a conference of pig farmers in Yorkshire, I was told beforehand that most of my audience would be owners or managers of such units.

The fourth item in order of purchase would be the pigs themselves and the feeding stuffs. Again, tax allowances are available when one comes to expand the size of the herd. Admittedly, the taxpayer is not called upon to pay for the feed, but any farming company or individual farmer large enough can secure favourable terms with one of the major companies – like Unilever or Rank Hovis McDougall – so that the cost of the first supply of feed is not paid for until the returns come in. Needless to say, the small farmer is seldom able to receive credit so favourably.

Now let us see what happens when someone wants to keep

pigs extensively, that is in fields rather than factories. The three hundred sows, instead of being kept on concrete in close quarters, will be out in the open, and about a hundred acres will be needed – more or less, depending on how well drained is the land. This is twenty times as much as an intensive unit, so the first item of expenditure will be, let us say, £200,000, and there are no tax allowances. Sow huts, fencing and other pieces of equipment will cost a fraction of what the intensive competitor will have paid out, perhaps less than £5,000, and that will bring relief from tax. In purchasing the herd and the feeding stuffs, both are placed on an equal footing. Straight away, it will be seen that in the matter of tax allowances, the factory farmer is able to set most of his capital expenditure against tax while the other farmer has virtually no such advantage at all. Yet, despite the great discrepancy of treatment, an appreciable number of arable farmers, especially when they have well drained downland, with underlying chalk to provide the drainage, are finding it profitable to establish outdoor herds. They are to be found in Berkshire, Oxfordshire, Wiltshire and Hampshire, especially on the higher land, usually acting as a break crop. A sow may eat a ton of concentrated feed in the course of a year, so the dung of a hundred sows concentrated on some thirty acres for a few months at a time should have the effect of enriching the soil. By suppressing the growth of weeds in that period, they also become natural herbicides. Anyone taking possession of a derelict smallholding years ago used to know the value of a few sows being turned out into the worst of the fields. The gain to the soil and natural advantage of such a break crop have enabled these outdoor herds to make a come-back. Anyone inspecting them would have to admit that, winter or summer, the sows look considerably more contented and healthier than their sisters in the sow stalls. If it is good farming, as experienced observers believe it to be, should it be penalised by the tax system?

The litters are born about twice a year, and, come weaning time, they are taken away from the sow and it is true that the young pigs are likely to be fattened intensively. But intensive fattening systems vary quite considerably. At one end, small groups of pigs are kept in comparatively large pens with access to fresh air. At the other, as many are kept together as practicable, in darkness to prevent fighting, and acute humidity. The spread of disease then becomes a major anxiety which can only be relieved by the constant use of antibiotics, both incorporated in the feed and administered as ordinary drugs. Medical opinion has expressed concern at the scale on which those antibiotics are used, and any sensible yardstick of efficiency must bring doubt as to whether the tax system is justified in extending its full support to what is going on.

A modern pig unit of a thousand sows in stalls and many thousands of pigs being fattened by ultra-intensive methods, employing only two or three men, all on a few acres of concrete, resembles a factory in more ways than one. The long arm of technology has stretched itself in, and has made it something quite different to the pig farm of twenty years ago when one man looked after thirty sows and made quite a good living. In one room there may be a computer adjusting feed levels daily for every sow, or performing some other function; in another room perhaps a closed circuit television set recording how the sows are farrowing; and in yet another there will be shelf upon shelf resembling a doctor's pharmacy. The employees don white coats; they look like – and they are – technicians. The sows are numbered and not named, and two or three essential statistics determine the life span, unlike the mixture of different criteria some years ago. All this is done in the name of efficiency, but it is also done with the aid of a tax system that does not choose to give comparable help to the farmer who is trying to compete using other methods; and if this aid were taken away it is extremely doubtful whether such a modern pig unit could survive. At least, no one in his right mind would invest £300,000 of his own capital in such a venture, nor any bank manager lend that money to him. Public money, directly or indirectly, has become available, and a branch of technology has stepped in to take advantage of what is offered.

Once the import levies were imposed upon feed stuffs, the need for further technological advances was made imperative. The pig farmer was now being put out by a high tax on his largest item of expenditure; and no matter how efficient he might be, he simply could not survive unless in every other item of expenditure he made drastic economies. In fact, they could not be made unless he enjoyed economies of scale. Hence the steady decline in the number of pig breeders after 1970. In 1971 there were, according to the Ministry's *Annual Review*, 62,900. By 1976 they had declined to 35,300, and in 1983 down still further to 20,600. Thus, in little over a decade, nearly two thirds of them have gone out of business, their efficiency notwithstanding.

A critic of what is being done is in danger of being dismissed as a latter-day Luddite, a fuddy-duddy reactionary who stands in the way of farming progress. A riposte like that misses the target. Putting to one side the question of whether a new technology should be encouraged when it promotes the inhumane treatment of animals, the most important consideration seems to be about the nature of efficiency. Is *Concorde* efficient? It is one of the supreme marvels of technology, but it still has to be paid for by somebody; and if the passenger cannot afford the fare, it seems rather hard that the rest of us, who have to stay at home, must pay the balance. Getting some little pig ready for the slaughter house two or three weeks quicker is efficient in much the same way as *Concorde*. It is marvellous, but not when we have to work out the true cost.

The economics of pig farming have afflicted my life for many years, and I am glad that those of the poultry world have passed me by. The essence is the same, but its effect is still worse. Looking after animals of any kind is a labour-intensive operation. To look after farm animals humanely, to get them to yield profitably, yet retain their health, demands patience, diligence, and understanding. Other qualities are needed too, and they add up to a combination that few of us possess. The humble hen makes that demand upon us, as does the dairy cow or the farrowing sow. Put tens of thousands of them together in one unit and no stockman on earth can practise the skills of good husbandry by himself. Modern technology has, however, stepped in and now one man can look after them profitably. The computer has invented hybrid hens that look alike, eat and drink alike and generally behave alike. That has been its purpose, and it has been very largely successful. I have to deny

total success for an anecdotal reason. I own a small farm which
is let and where the tenants keep about a dozen hens to supply
themselves and a few others with eggs, and they are housed in
an old fashioned movable chicken house in an open compound
of a few square yards. Each batch has come from a modern
poultry farm and, theoretically, they should behave alike. It is
noticeable that soon after they are released in the compound,
they develop distinct characters and their needs for food and
water begin to vary significantly. It might be added, they look
considerably healthier than those in the battery cages, and
moreover it is profitable to keep them to a much older age. Still,
it has to be admitted that technology has replaced husbandry;
and if profitability is the yardstick, it has been worthwhile,
because the methods it introduces are cheaper than employing
men and women.

Once we went over to a system of import levies on wheat and
maize, the day of the smaller producer came to an end. He was
still efficient in the sense that he could earn a livelihood without
a policy of price support, but not when the largest item in his
expenditure was grossly taxed. Statistics are not available to
show how the number of poultry producers has declined, but in
the *Annual Review* we find the number of poultry holdings for
each year. These are divided into those with laying fowls and
those with broilers, and each is further divided in size. Those
with fewer than a thousand laying fowls can be set aside as
unlikely to provide a livelihood and in all probability being a
subsidiary enterprise on the farm. So we should exclude them
and just take the number of holdings with broiler units and a
thousand or more laying fowls. We then find there were in 1967
12,500 such poultry farmers. In 1972, their number had fallen
to 9,400; and in 1977, they were down to 4,300. The most
recent figure is for 1982: it is down again, to 3,700.

According to the Ministry's *Annual Review*, in 1967 there
were 179,000 holdings with up to a thousand 'laying fowl'. This
was a high percentage of the total number of the agricultural
holdings which was 338,000 in that year. Of course, many were
kept for household needs, but five years later the number fell to
106,000. The inference must be that a large number of efficient
producers were being driven out because their flock ceased to
be profitable. This is confirmed by the sharp increase in the

number of large flocks in the same period. In 1967, only 39.9
per cent of all laying fowl were in flocks of over five thousand.
By 1973, the percentage had risen to 67.4 per cent. A few years
on the *Annual Reviews* had to increase the largest unit to twenty
thousand birds. In 1976, 50.2 per cent of laying fowls were in
flocks of twenty thousand or more; in 1983 the figure had
become 63.9 per cent. The broiler figures are even more
startling. In 1983, 55.4 per cent of broilers were in flocks of a
hundred thousand or more!

These trends have divorced poultry production from farming
in the ordinary sense of the word. Two large companies – the
Imperial Group and Unilever – through their subsidiaries took
over from the farmer's wife with her modest flock. That useful
supplement to the income of nearly every small farmer has been
removed by the tax system. A multi-million-pound commercial
concern can set up huge factory farms, each one keeping tens of
thousands of birds, and the cost of every item of the factory can
be written off against tax.

It has extended now to turkeys. Tens of thousands of farms
used to fatten about thirty or forty turkeys every year for the
Christmas market. They provided an extra job on the farm after
the harvest was in, and being housed in a barn or two or three
stables, they were easily attended to when the shorter days of
November and December came. In a word, they fitted very
neatly into the farming year, and they gave the farmer another
source of income that seldom failed him. For the work and risk
involved, the return was well worth his while. This convenient
sideline has gone. Two large companies have put up a series of
'turkey farms', and several of them are now in my constituency.
They consist of perhaps four or five acres, all concreted, and six
or so huge turkey houses, each taking up about half an acre, and
into them go thousands of baby turkeys. The land itself is
bought for 'agricultural use' and costs perhaps £12,000; all the
rest of it, the concreting, the erection of the buildings, the
putting in of all the plant and fittings can be set against tax by
these companies. The effective net cost to them of a 'farm'
costing £250,000 may be nearly halved.

The economies of scale achieved have to be acknowledged,
and they have given the public the chance to buy both eggs and
poultry meat at prices, in real terms, lower than those that

prevailed years ago. But how much lower would they be if the most expensive input was not taxed? If it is the case, as most producers claim, that feed costs are about 70 per cent of the total cost of production for most eggs and broilers, and the main part of the feed is taxed at a rate which varies between 50 per cent and 100 per cent, it must follow that getting rid of the tax would have two consequences. First, the price of eggs and poultry meat would fall substantially and the public would be able to buy more of both of them. Secondly, the pressure upon the poultry producers to adopt the more aggressive and intensive methods of husbandry would diminish. Lower costs would have a relaxing effect upon the producer; and the consumer would be the beneficiary – and also millions of birds.

Neither British eggs nor British poultry meat, whether in the form of turkeys, geese, ducks or chickens, have at any time required protection from the world market. Their producers have been efficient in the sense that I have defined it, literally throughout history. Indeed, this has been the most efficient branch of British agriculture. Yet in the last year or so it has become generally unprofitable, and only the very largest concerns have avoided losing money. The only protection the poultry producers need is protection from the grain lobby.

To some extent it is understandable that pig and poultry farmers have been victims of the policy, for the CAP itself has made no attempt to support and protect them as it has the others. Of them all, it might be said that the dairy farmer seems to have been the most cushioned. He has had a guaranteed price for every drop of milk his cows produce, import levies to tax cheap New Zealand butter, a prohibition upon the importation of other butter from abroad, subsidies to make our own butter artificially cheaper, besides grants and other kinds of financial support to help him along. In fact, it has been of little avail. The same trend is to be seen as in other kinds of farming: the small men squeezed out and the large ones made larger still.

In 1950 I went off to learn about dairy farming. Fifteen cows – no more, no less – was the size of the herd on an eighty-acre holding. Its story holds the essence of what has gone wrong with British agriculture, so let it be told. In the first place, it was very efficient. By that I mean its owner made a good livelihood without collecting a penny's worth of government aid. That may be difficult to believe three decades later, when dairy farmers may have a herd of over a hundred cows to make a reasonable living; but he could afford three or four hunters and, in the winter months, he went out with the Quorn or Belvoir, usually three times a week, sometimes four. Of course, on a hunting day he got up earlier and returned in time for the evening milking. True, half of the farm was in the Quorn country and the other half in the Belvoir, so he could claim the farmer's privilege of hunting for nothing. Yet in many other ways he led a very comfortable life. Fifteen cows did not take up much of his time; he was never in a hurry when callers came and he never grudged spending the time of day with them. (How different it is now, when a farm entrance so often sports a board saying 'No callers without appointment' or 'Representatives must telephone first' – in the 1950s we never saw such notices in the countryside.) Nor did he have any worries that I can remember. He certainly never had an overdraft and would never have had cause to visit his bank manager.

The milk yields would have been about two thirds of today's average, perhaps less. In the months when the herd were out on the summer grass, the yield would be higher; in winter the yield would fall because hay was the principal feed and bought-in compounds were scarcely used. Thus the eighty acres fed the cows with most of their needs. There was one elderly tractor that might have fetched £10 at a sale; it was good enough for the harrowing and rolling and the hay making. All the machinery used in the course of the year could not have been worth much above £100. No fertilisers went on the land, except the manure from the cows and hunters; no herbicides except the swish of the scythe or, if the weeds were really bad – which I do not remember them ever being – the tractor and grass cutter could be brought into use.

His expenses were trifling. There was simply very little he needed to purchase. It was a shamelessly low-cost system. Every month a cheque for the milk came in: it was his gross income, and his net taxable income was not much less. He paid income tax, I believe, for those were the days when we did not have the present array of tax allowances to tempt the farmer into buying expensive machinery and equipment. He paid into the Treasury funds and he took nothing out. Judged as a businessman, he was successful: he made a profit every year.

No welfarist could have complained at the way his cows were kept; no environmentalist could have demurred at his hedgerows and the hundreds of birds living on his acres; and no conservationist raised his eyebrows at the absence of sprays and chemicals. Neighbouring farmers considered him perfectly normal – just like themselves. In fact, there would have been in the 1950s, and even in the 1960s, tens of thousands of dairy farmers running their farms as he did.

I had assumed that in the 1980s all that had disappeared and claimed as much to a farming audience in Kent not long ago. I was told that there was just such a farm not far from Ashford; two families ran it together. One interesting point emerged from the discussion – everyone in the farming world had dismissed them as cranks, but some of their neighbours were now beginning to see some sense in what they were doing.

The farming establishment will still think them cranky; NFU leaders will dismiss them as inefficient; ADAS officials shake their heads and call them hopeless, while the salesmen from the agrobusinesses will pass them by as loonies. When the leaders of agriculture smirk at farmers who make a profit without taxpayers' money, while they give their respect to those who cannot make a livelihood out of their farm unless given ever more government money as each year goes by, other people may wonder whether their sense of values has gone awry. In no other branch of the nation's economy is there a similar attitude of mind. Why, we might ask, is it so in agriculture? It is the policy makers who have set the tone, uttered the exhortations, laid down the lines to be taken and, of course, taken the money from the taxpayer. It is difficult to think of anywhere else to put the blame.

So far as the Ministry of Agriculture is concerned, one cow to the acre was considered in the 1960s a sensible aim. For a dairy farmer to attain what seemed to be a four-fold increase in productivity, a quite different system of husbandry was needed. To begin with, another breed of cow would have to be bought. Off to slaughter would go the low-cost Dairy

Shorthorns, Red Polls and Ayrshires and in their place would come the Friesians. The old pastures must be ploughed up and reseeded; and the new kinds of grass heavily fertilised and sprayed with chemicals. The high stocking density made the new grass too valuable to be poached when the rain fell, so the cattle must spend much of the year indoors. That meant that expensive new buildings must go up and yards be concreted, and as the risk of disease is then made considerably greater, the animals must be frequently treated with antibiotics and other drugs. This last element has given birth to a substantial sub-industry, whose sales to farmers have reached many millions of pounds. To maintain the high stocking rate and gain the extra high yields of milk, expensive feedingstuffs are also purchased. Finally, to have one man employed looking after fifteen or twenty cows becomes totally unprofitable, so expensive machinery is introduced to enable one man to look after seventy-five cows or more. Thus jobs are lost in the countryside and gained in the cities where the machinery is made – as often as not in some other country.

If enough has not already been said to question whether the dairy farmer has benefited from protection, perhaps a few hard figures will suffice. In 1967 there were 131,600 dairy farmers and more than half of them (71,300) had fewer than twenty cows. In the following five years the total number of dairy farmers had fallen to 98,700 and only 41,000 of them had herds of less than twenty. Today there are so few herds of that size that their numbers are no longer recorded in the *Annual Review*. Still, we are told that 18,300 herds of fewer than thirty cows exist; that altogether there are only 57,700 dairy farmers, and the average size of herd has risen to 55.

None of this is to suggest that we ought to revert to herds of less than twenty, though that would soon get rid of the milk surplus. But it does establish that in 1967 there were twice as many dairy farmers able to make a livelihood as there are today. Moreover, they were economically efficient and common sense persuades one that many of them have been driven out of dairying because the largest item in their budget is now heavily taxed. Laurence Gould Agricultural Consultants have estimated that in the next ten years another 14,000 dairy farmers will be forced to give up. That means that 43,000 will be left, one third of what there were in 1967.

A neighbour of mine has forty acres and, shame on him, only twenty-five cows. It is a Guernsey herd, one of the finest in the country, perhaps even in the world. His cattle have won numerous championships and been exported to faraway countries, and he himself has travelled abroad to judge the breed at the foremost shows. The stock on his farm are very special, they have been seen on television and even the most untutored observer would notice how well they look. It is the fruit of good husbandry, many hours given to the herd each week by father and son beyond what is commercially necessary. Watch them at work and you will see they are superbly good stockmen: quiet spoken and gentle, proud to have bred such animals and caring very much about how they are treated.

Because this farmer is a tenant, few tax allowances come his way, nor does he get any grants or subsidies, and the effect of the import levies in his case is that the feedingstuffs cost him £3,500 more than they would otherwise. This is a particular burden to him, for the income he and his son live upon is derisory. Getting up each day at 5 a.m. and working on to the end of the evening milking, his hourly rate of pay is about one quarter of what a factory worker receives. With costs continuing to go up and his income standing still, the squeeze makes the remedy plain: keep more cows and produce more milk. Lower standards of husbandry would follow, and then it would be pointless for him to keep such a prize-winning herd. So if the present policy goes on, there will be one of two courses of action for him to take. He will have to decide whether to be ruthlessly commercial and, with a different, high-yielding breed of cow, produce the extra milk we do not want – or to give up dairy farming altogether.

'But,' the apologist will say, 'all this is about the livestock farmer. What about the arable sector?' Here we are assured it would be darkness and gloom if the price mechanism were to take charge and the present system of support were taken away. Indeed, there would be trouble for all those farmers who have abandoned stock and gone over to arable crops at the behest of the policy maker – because they have been diverted from efficient to inefficient farming. But the day of reckoning must come for them sooner or later. It will come when the kindly taxpayer decides that to go on subsidising, at increasing cost, the production of food we do not want to eat is a silly waste of public money at a time when cuts must be imposed upon schools, hospitals, road-building and other forms of public expenditure that most rational people believe to be more worthwhile. Enough is enough, the taxpayer may say: that one puff of wind and the castle of cards falls down

Generally speaking, the farmers we are now discussing are the arable farmers with Grade III land or even worse. All our agricultural land has been graded into five qualities. The Ministry of Agriculture set up a Study Group on Agricultural Classification, formed of twelve experts drawn from the Ministry, and in 1966 its considered views were published, together with a definition of each grade of land.

Only 2.8 per cent of all our farmland qualifies as Grade I, and a very large part of it is in my constituency, the Parts of Holland being largely formed by the deposits of rich alluvial silt. This is 'land of exceptional quality', as good as any on our planet, and capable of growing any temperate crop in an efficient and profitable way. Not far behind is Grade II, and 14.6 per cent of our agricultural land comes within this definition of 'land of high quality'. It also can produce all temperate crops efficiently and profitably, the margin between it and Grade I being of little significance except to the experienced eye. Using either grade of land for any purpose other than the growing of food verges upon sacrilege. Those fortunate enough to farm such land, assuming a modest competence and a little luck, should earn a fair return from any crop they grow.

'Should', however, is the operative word. The present system works against the small farmer regardless of the high quality land he may have, and in the longer term it provides unfair competition for even the largest farmer with such land. Taking the latter first, the present policy has caused most of our Grade III land to grow arable crops, especially wheat, barley and oil seed rape. 48.9 per cent of our farmland is so classified. It was defined by the Study Group as 'land of average quality with

65

limitations due to the soil, relief or climate'; and after describing its defects, the experts concluded that 'in fact, some of the best quality permanent grassland may be placed in this Grade, where the physical characteristics of the land make arable cropping inadvisable.'

Nothing could be much plainer. Between our good land in Grades I and II and the land in Grade III there is a clear distinction: the quality of the first makes it wholly suitable for arable crops, but the average nature of the latter renders it more appropriate for pasture. Of course, there are variations in Grade III; much of it has been drained thoroughly (with public money) and so long as the draining remains effective and so long as plenty of fertilisers are applied, such crops as wheat, barley, potatoes and sugar beet can be produced with moderate success. Generally speaking, however, it is simply not possible for an arable farmer to earn a reasonable income out of Grade III land unless the kindly taxpayer helps him.

Grade IV and Grade V are even worse. Yet one can see wheat and barley growing on both. The Study Group defined Grade IV land as 'land with severe limitations due to adverse soil, relief or climate. . . . Generally only suitable for low output enterprises'. 19·7 per cent of our farmland is so classified. The remaining 14 per cent is Grade V, and should, at best, carry a few sheep or perhaps some of those splendid Highland cattle. Yet I have heard the Deputy-President of the NFU claim with pride that he was growing barley on such land. Given enough money from the taxpayer, one might grow a few ears of corn around Eros's statue; and one wonders how much has been paid out by way of grants, subsidies and tax allowances to enable that miserable soil of his to produce yet more tons of surplus barley.

But it is unfair competition of the grossest kind. We need a certain quantity of barley every year for malting and animal feed; and a sensible policy would try to make sure that it was made available at the lowest cost, and grown by the most efficient producers. In other words, if home grown barley is to be used, our farmers with Grade I and Grade II land should come first in the market. Instead a kind of handicap race has emerged, those who would otherwise be hopelessly behind in the race being given so much support that they are able to keep alongside the natural winners. So long as we actually need these arable crops to be grown, no particular damage is done to the efficient, but come a system of quotas to curb the surpluses and the unfairness would be plain enough for even the Deputy-President of the NFU to see.

Forty or fifty acres of rented land of Grade I or Grade II quality used to afford a good livelihood. That was before the present policy came about. In my constituency there were hundreds of farmers with no more land than that and many with less than half as much; and though they may never have been rich, they were certainly not poor. They were also efficient, that is to say, they were able to make a livelihood from the land without public money.

Not many of them survive today. Apart from the import levies to protect those growing wheat and barley, not a single one of the many other forms of support has served their interests. They would fail to qualify for the grants and subsidies because they were deemed too small or because they were tenants or because their forms of farming were ineligible or the sum of money, being related to the size of the holding, would not be worth the paperwork to apply for. The tax allowances have positively worked against them. Because they entitle a farmer to write off one hundred per cent of the cost of his machinery against one year's income tax, the manufacturers have been able to increase their prices far beyond the rate of inflation, and the cost of even the smallest new tractor now exceeds the taxable income of a small farmer.

Thus hundreds of efficient small arable farmers in my constituency, and many others elsewhere, with Grade I and Grade II land have gone out of business. Instead they may be driving a lorry or helping to make diesel engines in Peterborough, or they may have joined the swelling ranks of local government. Is the nation's economy the better for the change? The victims' opinion seems to be that they themselves are not.

Our arable farmers with Grade I and Grade II land are a diminishing band: only a few thousand of them exist. Technically they are extremely competent and, given world prices, they would be efficient. But even those of them prospering under the present system are now getting near to a danger point. In 1939 the average yield of wheat was 18·3 hundredweight to the acre. On this good land it has become three or four tons, and it is rising year by year. What will happen when it reaches six tons to the acre, as predicted by agricultural scientists for the 1990s? New varieties of wheat and new advances in cultivation are on the way, and the Continental farmer will not be so far behind. The present surpluses will look like molehills.

Some kind of control will have to be exercised. Several are being canvassed. A tax on nitrogenous fertilisers is one. But this will bear more heavily on our arable farmers than those in the rest of the Common Market where their use is much less. A device for limiting surpluses which forces British agriculture to grow less in proportion to competitors in the same market will be unfair.

An obvious remedy is reduction in farmgate prices. Of all the alternatives, this would suit our efficient farmers the most. Lower prices would not drive them out of business, but it would mean the end of many of the smaller arable farmers on the Continent. The remedy would be 'efficient' but the Common Agricultural Policy is meant to be about keeping farmers on the land, and the other nine Agricultural Ministers would almost certainly oppose this step. Electorally it would be disastrous for some of them.

It is for this reason that some arrangement of quotas is considered in Brussels to be the most acceptable brake on increasing production. There are two major objections for our efficient arable farmers. The first concerns how quotas can be supervised. Whether the quota is on acreages or tonnage, the opportunity for a grower to be less than totally honest will be at hand. Is some official to tour around making sure it is thirty and not thirty-five acres that is planted? If the quota is of tonnages, its sale can be to all manner of outlets. Perhaps a regulation might be passed requiring all the wheat to be sold to specified merchants; but the wheat need not be sold at all; it can be used as feed on the farm or exchanged with a neighbouring farmer who wants feed and in return does some contract work. The possibilities for cheating are so many that it is difficult to believe that the temptations will be resisted. I have a suspicion that a few of our own farmers would do so with a perfectly clear conscience; they will be utterly convinced that the French are cheating, so why shouldn't they!

The second objection is particularly serious for those with Grade I or Grade II land. Quotas will be intended to restrict all growers, that is all who grow wheat today. This includes tens of thousands of British farmers with Grade III, IV, or even V land who have only gone over from keeping stock to growing wheat because the system of import levies makes it more profitable. They too will receive a quota like the naturally efficient farmer. The quota must be fixed at an amount less than what was being grown, perhaps 90 per cent. Are all growers then given a quota pro rata? If so, the efficient farmer on Grade I and Grade II land is required by law to grow less of what he can grow efficiently; and the inefficient farmer is allowed to go on growing wheat he can only grow inefficiently. Both must look for alternative crops. It seems objectionable that the efficient farmer should be put to the task in the same way as his inefficient competitor. The only fair quota system would be one that allowed the farmer with Grade I and Grade II land to grow as much as before and required the great majority with the lower Grades to grow a great deal less. Then it would have the same effect as the price mechanism, but that of course would clash with the objectives of the Common Agricultural Policy.

Our efficient arable farmers may feel comfortable today. Tomorrow life will be different. The 1990s will soon be here, and the time has come for our efficient arable farmers with top quality land to think very seriously whether their interests are going to be served by the present system continuing.

5/War Between Allies

When the government of a country allows its people to trade freely with others who live beyond its frontiers, it makes it possible for links to be forged. There cannot be trade without communication; and the very moment we begin to talk to people in another country, the barriers that have kept us apart must start to come down. As trade increases, the links get stronger. There are exchanges of visits and meetings together. Then follows the discussion of markets, of what suits the consumer in one country and not the other, and all the problems of commercial dealings. As the talks go on, an understanding grows up in each party of the other's country and its way of doing things. The narrow question of how much is to be paid for the goods is left behind, as many matters about the two countries are discussed and understood.

While the people of the two countries talk together and the talks lead to satisfactory trade between them, which in turn brings to both a higher degree of prosperity, sheer self-interest must reduce the prospect of the two countries wanting to fight a war against each other. So when a government lets its people trade unrestrictedly with the people of another country, it is making a declaration of peace.

Is the converse equally true? Let us see what must follow when a government takes away from its people the freedom of trade that they have hitherto enjoyed. It says to its people 'Until now you have traded freely with those who live in Ruritania, but you will do so no longer. We shall put a tax upon the food you import from Ruritania and also place a limit on the amount you will be allowed to buy from the Ruritanians who supply you.' Put in such words it may sound a trifle whimsical, yet substitute the United States for Ruritania and it is what scores of firms, whose business was founded upon imports from the US, have been told. Wheat, maize, beef, butter, cheese, dried fruit, tinned fruit such as pineapples and peaches, and even fresh food such as apples, used to be imported without any restriction at all. Free trade in food used to be complete and absolute. The Wheat Act in 1932 made a slight difference to the amount that came in, the policy of deficiency payments indirectly reduced supplies, and so also did a few other measures introduced by the UK Government; but until we decided to go over to a system of import levies and import duties, preparatory to entering the EEC, a policy of free trade in food generally prevailed between the United States and ourselves.

It is beyond doubt that the farmers of North America are able to grow wheat and maize more cheaply than we can ourselves. It is not that they are, in any technical sense, more efficient than our own farmers; it is simply that nature has given them advantages denied to us. Both Canada and the US have many millions of acres of soil that are excellent for growing wheat and maize, and a climate that is as perfect for the purpose as one could wish for. Just as our mild and wet climate can afford us good grassland, so their cold winters followed by their hot summers are better for cereals. Their cold winter puts a curb upon the diseases afflicting crops, while we have to spray our land with herbicides and other toxic chemicals on a scale that increases every year, as do its costs and dangers. The hot summers on the other side of the Atlantic enable the harvest to be garnered without it being dried, while we use corn driers, each one now costing many thousands of pounds. True, the farmers can write off the entire financial cost of it against his income tax in one year; but the economic cost remains, and it is insidiously paid for by the British public as taxpayers and consumers. There are other advantages of climate conferred upon North American grain growers; and maybe the most important is the sun never fails to shine down upon the ripening corn at the time it is most needed. Oh lucky Americans! What would our arable men give for such solar comfort.

Yet 82,000,000 acres of the United States were set aside – as the euphemism goes – in 1983. It is an area the size of Texas and about twice the total area of our own farm land. It is an area capable of growing arable crops at low cost. And all of it was taken out of cultivation to lie fallow for at least a year. The Federal Government decreed that it should be done, and its Payment-in-Kind programme was intended to compensate the US farmer for being forbidden to do his work.

In return for the farmer agreeing not to cultivate his land, the US Department of Agriculture bought his previous year's crop of wheat and maize and gave it back to him so that he could sell it the following year, and in the meanwhile offer it as security for money he needed to borrow. The total cost of this and some other forms of aid cost the US taxpayer about $18,000 millions. It is about half the true cost of supporting the farmers in the EEC. If the world were a more sensible place there would be no need to give the American farmer a single dime; and any artificial propping up with public money would simply be unnecessary. He would be certain of a place in the world market, and as a low cost producer, he rather than anyone else would supply the demand. Instead, the opposite is happening. The world not being a sensible place, at least so far as agriculture is concerned, the American farmer has become a charge upon the US taxpayer, and his income is steadily going down and his indebtedness to the bank is going up to a level that is putting at risk a large part of the US banking system.

US farm incomes have plummetted down. In the last ten years they have fallen to less than half of what they were in real terms. According to *Agricultural Outlook*, January/February 1984, published by the US Department of Agriculture, total net farm income in 1974 was $23,700 millions; in two years the total fell to $15,200 millions; by 1982 it had gone down to $10,700 millions, and it seems likely to be about the same for 1983. This collapse has had a devastating effect upon their standard of living. Resentment is widespread and it has naturally made them ask several questions. Why has it happened? Who is responsible? How much longer must they experience this decline into poverty? To what extent are they themselves at fault? They cannot sensibly accuse themselves. They remain the same kind of farmers they have been for decades: the lowest-cost producers of wheat and maize. And their low costs should still enable them to overcome fair competition from any quarter of the globe.

Resentment extends beyond the farmstead. Tens of thousands of businesses that service and supply the US farmer are no less affected, the manufacturers and dealers in machinery and fertilisers are obvious examples. Agriculture is the only industry over a vast area of the United States: it is the mainspring of the economy of over half the States. So when the purchasing power of the farmer falls by over a third, the effect upon every business and professional man throughout most of the United States is serious. He too asks who is responsible.

Nobody has become more anxious than the bank manager. Total indebtedness by the farmers reached $194,900 million in 1982, an increase of 11 per cent over the previous year. As there are 2,400,000 farmers, this represents an average debt of $812,208 and that compares with some £20,000 for our own farmers. Averages can conceal a dangerous truth and the dangerous truth in this case is that 1,464,000 of the US farmers (that is 60 per cent) sold no more than $20,000 worth of produce in 1981. So their indebtedness is dangerously out of proportion to their capacity to repay what they have borrowed. If they cannot pay the interest charges and their debts continue to grow, the consequences facing those banks in the US that depend upon the fortunes of agriculture are deeply serious. In fact, no bank, not even the most powerful, is isolated from the impending crisis. Unless some change of fortune comes, it is no longer fanciful to speak of a crash comparable to that of 1929.

The US Department of Agriculture publishes each year a 'Fact Book of US Agriculture'. The issue for 1983 sets out most of the figures that I have given, but also many others to show how important agriculture is to the US economy. In 1981 39 per cent of their crops were exported, worth $43,800 million. In both 1982 and 1983 there was a substantial fall. As America is the world's largest food exporter, and dependent upon food more than any other kind of export for her trade abroad, any fall in food exports is going to cause the value of the dollar to go down. Wheat and maize are most important factors in this. In 1981 US wheat exports were worth $8,000 million and together with maize and other commodities for animal feed made up more than 60 per cent of the total exports of farm products. There was a time when we used to be one of the principal markets for this wheat and maize. That, of course, was before 1973, when the system of import levies and import duties was put fully in effect. In 1972 we imported 788,004 tonnes of wheat and 1,645,173 tonnes of maize from the United States. In 1983 it was 18,444 tonnes of wheat and 709,021 tonnes of maize. Since US wheat costs about two-thirds of the price of ours, the fall in our purchases is some measure of how much our most basic of foods is being taxed.

A weak or unstable dollar should be a matter of concern for us in Britain. The more it falls against the pound, the more expensive our exports become in the United States and the less the Americans are likely to buy from us. When the value of a nation's currency goes down in the foreign exchange market, it is an informal, and legitimate, form of protectionism. Invariably it is accompanied by a demand for formal, and not so legitimate, protectionist measures: non-tariff barriers are devised to keep out imports.

If America's share of the world's food trade continues to decline, if her exports to the EEC continue to be heavily penalised, and if her exports elsewhere are continually forced to compete with surpluses dumped by the EEC, the dollar must become chronically weaker than it deserves to be. It is a matter that the US State Department cannot overlook, for we know the strength or weakness of a country's foreign policy is to some extent determined by the strength or weakness of its currency. In 1983, the US trade deficit reached the staggering height of $49 thousand millions and in 1984 the US Treasury reckons it may exceed $100 thousand millions!

If the dollar still appears 'strong' against most other currencies including our own today, this is due to a cause which cannot benefit the US economy – the inordinately high interest rates that have enticed considerable amounts of money from Europe and elsewhere. These high rates have stifled the American businessman desiring to expand, and so long as he is faced with them he cannot play his full part in taking his country out of recession. The prosperity of all industries is set back. The outer strength of the dollar stems from an inner weakness; and it cannot be sustained.

The US Department of Labour is also anxious. 23,000,000

Americans work in some phase of food production; and in the actual growing of food in the fields, more Americans are engaged than the combined number in the steel, automobile and transport industries. In providing feeds, fertilisers and other supplies to agriculture, no less than 5,000,000 Americans are employed. Altogether one American in 5 working in the private sector works in or for agriculture. The United States cannot prosper, and its people cannot enjoy full employment, unless it is the principal exporter of food to the markets of the world. Unemployment has bedevilled the US economy as it has ours; the evil is receding, but only slightly. Were its agriculture to be allowed by the EEC to face fair competition, the US would be in a position to lead the free world out of the recession. Commentators speak of the US being in that position in the immediate future; but such talk is futile while the EEC denies fair competition to the largest and most naturally efficient agriculture that any nation in the world is able to enjoy.

The third US Department affected is the Treasury. As the country's largest industry, agriculture has been called upon to pay a high proportion of the nation's revenue. The US Government could not permit what we in Britain have – our farmers taking out of the Treasury more than they put in. Because of our system of one hundred per cent tax allowances for new plant and machinery and the setting off of all interest charges against profits, any large farmer in the UK can avoid income tax altogether, and many do so, even though their incomes may run into tens of thousands of pounds.

The US farmers, on the contrary, are expected to pay their share of taxes. In 1981 they paid $3,800 million in federal and state income taxes and about $344 million in sales tax. (The latter is the counterpart of our VAT from which our farmers are exempted.) In addition to income tax, there is a personal property tax in the United States and in 1981 their farmers paid $759 million towards this. The fourth tax is on farm real estate and in 1981 it took from them $3,800 million. Thus the US farmer contributed a total of $8,703 million in taxation in 1981. With farm incomes down by over one third since then, the Treasury will be fortunate to receive money on that scale for 1984. Worse than that, the farmers have become like ours –

taking out more than they are putting in. The PiK programme is a heavy burden upon federal funds and the rest of the American economy must be taxed to pay for it. There are some crazy economists about, but not even the craziest would argue that this is the way to speed the country out of the recession.

Politically, the government must reckon with the fact that the 82 million acres taken out of cultivation represent 8 per cent of all American farm land, and the largest part of it is good arable land lying in the Mid-West, in the States that a Republican must win to be elected. Nearly half the farms in that area may have idle acres.

One needs to visit some part of those 82,000,000 acres to understand the enormity of the 'set aside' programme. I had the opportunity in 1983: I flew over some of that rich land and also travelled by road, seeing it close at hand. What farmer will happily watch his land go to waste, even if the Government pays him to do it? As the Presidential elections draw near, many thousands of Republican farmers are going to feel frustrated and resentful. They know who is to blame and the President knows they know. They expect him to fight for their interests. Most political fights are within the frontiers of a country, but not this one. The fight is with the EEC and the battleground will not be in Congress but in places like Japan, Mexico, Korea, China, the USSR, Taiwan, Spain, Egypt, Venezuela, and Brazil, where they like to buy their imported food at the cheapest price, regardless of how much it may be subsidised by the government of the producing country.

Wheat and maize, it might be added, are not the only items in a future food war. Dairy produce is the second most important, after cattle, to the US farmers. The total amount received by all US farmers for dairy produce is over $18,000 millions and unless a substantial proportion of it is exported, the second largest part of the country's agriculture is put in jeopardy. Their inability to sell their farm produce abroad is undoubtedly the main reason for the US trade deficit.

Retaliation can take a very simple form: the United States will be able to do what the EEC does and subsidise its exports, and so regain the market it has lost. It will feel totally justified. In 1976 the EEC's share of world food exports was 8 per cent, almost the whole of it gained by undercutting competitors with the aid of subsidies from the guarantee fund of the CAP. By 1982, the share had more than doubled to 17 per cent, thus making the EEC the largest exporter after the United States. Every inch of this progress has been made by using more taxpayers' money to increase the subsidies, and most of the inches gained by the EEC were inches lost by the United States. In the three years 1980-1982, the EEC spent £8,700 million, or about £8,000,000 a day, on subsidising food exports. It means that more than half the money the EEC spends goes on trying to take away the trade – and the livelihood – of farmers who live in other countries. Australia, New Zealand, Canada and a host of poorer countries in the Third World have been too weak to retaliate by matching subsidy with subsidy, at least not on the massive scale of the EEC. So they have lost their markets, and are the poorer for it. The EEC is also the poorer for what it has done; it has no more money available for the fight unless the member states agree to ask their taxpayers to pay still more money. Its budget ceiling has been reached. The United States is in a more favourable position. Were the President to ask Congress for more money to save the nation's farmers, there is little doubt what the answer would be. Uncle Sam can fight back, and he can win. Defeat for the EEC would be certain.

Let us look next at Latin America for another example of what happens when historic ties are cut by protectionism. The amount of trade that took place between Argentina and ourselves used to be immense. It was British businessmen, engineers and other experts who gave the Argentine economy the size and shape it enjoyed. For nearly a century we purchased beef in quantities that increased year by year, and the more we purchased, the more dependent they became upon us. Although they imported many of their needs from us, a large part of their beef was paid for by increased investment, in railways, property, banking and other forms that enhanced Argentina's wealth. We also imported wheat and several other commodities from her, so that altogether Britain was her best customer. Argentinian prosperity depended on the British people.

Then came our entry into the Common Market. Within two

77

years our imports from Argentina were cut in half, from £106,000,000 in 1973 to £53,000,000 in 1975. They continued to go down and within a few years were of trifling importance. The effect upon Argentina was appalling. Unemployment rose; bankruptcies became common; government revenue declined; and every part of her agriculture, her main source of wealth, was blighted. Cattle ranching covers about half of the total land area of Argentina; one third of her exports used to be meat and agriculture contributed ninety per cent of her export income. The EEC tariff of 70 pence on each pound of Argentina's meat was a punishing blow. It was an aggressive and hurtful act, from which Argentina's economy has not recovered. Soviet Russia, never backward when trouble brews between the West and a Third World country, quietly moved in with a trade delegation. In due course, her Embassy in Buenos Aires became a place of some importance: politicians found it more helpful than ours.

Now for all those years that we traded so amicably with Argentina, a thousand or more settlers from the British Isles were on the Falkland Islands. Britain and Argentina were prospering together, and the economic alliance kept us clear of open conflict. Today the Falklands dispute remains unresolved. The Argentine claim has not been abandoned, and the cost to us of coping with the threat it poses is going to run into hundreds of millions of pounds. It will be the equivalent of many, many years of beef supplies. So long as the British consumer is denied the supply of cheap beef from Argentina, which means so long as we subscribe to the CAP, and so long as the British taxpayer has to pay these massive sums of money to ward off the Argentinians, we are entitled to ask one or two questions. Would Argentina, while so dependent upon her export trade with us for her prosperity, have deliberately cut off that trade? What could she have gained by acquiring those bleak islands when she could have lost so much? Common sense seems to suggest that the British people would have remained blissfully unaware of the Falklands if the economic alliance with Argentina had not been severed by us in 1973.

The other question is, what would happen over the Falklands were we to open our ports to Argentinian food again? That impoverished, bankrupt country would have a chance of recovery; its farmers and meat processors would be glad enough to respond, and no Argentinian government would be so short sighted as to stand in the way. An economic alliance would begin again, hesitatingly at first perhaps, but as it grew, so would the threat to the Falklands recede. The British taxpayer would be able to spend his money, and the British serviceman his time, in other ways.

What of Australia, New Zealand and Canada? Going over to Canada for the first time, in 1983, I met an elderly Canadian, brought up on an English farm, who had, like so many other younger sons, had to leave his home as a young man to farm abroad, 'to go to the colonies'. By the time war came in 1939, he was just established on land that had taken some years to bring into economic cultivation. The Canadian government then decreed that, as part of the war effort, the farmers would sell their wheat to the UK – 'to the people back home' – at thirty cents a bushel below the world price. They did not demur; they did it gladly and their sons went off to fight as well. By the time the war was over, the discount had caused the Canadian wheat growers to forfeit no less than $600,000,000. Given that a dollar was worth a great deal more in 1945, it represented quite a fortune to every farmer.

Within two years our system of deficiency payments began the process of displacing their exports to us and, at the same time, putting a gentle squeeze upon the price we paid them. Once deficiency payments gave way to import levies on wheat, the gentle squeeze became more like strangulation. As our own high cost production of cereals increased, so their exports to us diminished. They looked elsewhere for their sales, and they were not always successful. Within three years the Canadian government had to tell its farmers to grow less wheat and to punish them if they disobeyed.

I passed on to the Canadian Minister of Agriculture what we in Britain were being repeatedly told, but which I suspected to be a falsehood, namely that Canada had found other markets for her wheat and was no longer interested in ours. His denial was plain and blunt; a minute later he said how sad he was that Canada and Britain had moved so far apart that statements such as that could be made. The fact is, we are being forced apart by a policy that has deliberately cut off trade between us. As a result we no longer meet and talk together as we used to do, and misunderstandings arise, even mistrust. It should never have been necessary for me to pass on that information to the Minister, nor for him to reply as he did. The alliance is weakened; perhaps the Canadian attitude at the time of the Falklands conflict showed how weak it had become.

The amount of low cost food entering Britain from Canada used to be considerable. Before we imposed import levies and import duties on their exports, shiploads of wheat, cheese, apples and tinned salmon used to come over to the benefit of the British people. How different it is today. The drop in wheat imports has made both our countries the poorer. We are also both the poorer as a result of our huge surpluses having to be exported. Canada, like the United States, Argentina and Australia, has been forced out of her export market by the EEC's policy of dumping.

The cost to the public in the EEC for every tonne exported is some £30-60 by way of subsidy, that being usually the difference between our cost of production and that of the four countries that grow wheat cheaper than anyone else. Unless there is a change of policy, the surplus from Britain alone is likely to double within a few years. *NAC News*, published by the Royal Agricultural Society of England, in February 1983, under the heading 'Gearing up for Grain Exports', said: 'This season we have an exportable surplus of cereals of some 5 million tonnes. In a few years' time it could easily be over 10 million tonnes. The export market will therefore be an additional outlet for British grain for many years to come.'

Every ounce of that grain will displace a legitimate export from a low cost country, whose farmers' fortunes are already in decline as a direct result of our dumping.

In cutting our trade links with Canada we have made certain that our own manufacturing industries will be the casualties. In my visit to Canada in 1983, I cannot remember seeing a single motor vehicle manufactured in England. I did, however, see scores of Renaults, Citroens, Volkswagens, Fiats and others from the Continent. I was told that ten years ago our cars would have been seen in far greater numbers than those, in every city and village. The reason was that they entered Canada free of duty, under the Commonwealth Preference System, while vehicles from outside the United States or the Commonwealth had a tariff of 17 per cent imposed upon them. Such a tariff was enough to exclude, almost entirely, any car made in the EEC as it then existed.

As part of the campaign to take us into the Common Market, Lord Stokes, then Chairman of British Leyland, arranged to have inserted in our leading newspapers full-page advertisements telling the readers that British Leyland's future depended upon our membership of the EEC, that it was poised to capture a new market, and in doing so, this great British company would become still greater and even more prosperous. Failure to join the Common Market would have, we were told, most deplorable consequences; thousands would lose their jobs and much else. I began a correspondence with Lord Stokes, and while I agreed that British Leyland might be able to compete on equal terms within the Common Market, I asked him whether the loss of the tariff preference in Canada would not give our Continental competitors an equal advantage. It is quite apparent from his reply that neither he nor his advisers had considered the point. His principal adviser on the matter was one of the most ardent of the vast tribe of Euro-enthusiasts and he continued the correspondence on the basis that no market other than the EEC was of much consequence.

Not only cars, but all our manufactures, previously exported to Canada under preferential terms, have been affected adversely. When we deliberately put up barriers against Canada, we made it inevitable that we ourselves would get hurt. Only a small part of the export trade we lost in that way has been diverted to the Common Market: most of it has been lost altogether, and as a direct result, many thousands of jobs in Britain have also been lost. In fact, the diversion of trade to the EEC has been much less than is claimed. From the Overseas Trade Statistics, the Cambridge Monograph and other sources one can calculate the proportion of our exports that go to the original Six. In 1972 it was 21·9 per cent, rising to 25·3 per cent in 1974. If one excludes the oil exports to the original Six, it is now 25·1 per cent. Instead of a gain, there has been a slight fall of 0·2 per cent in the export of manufactured goods to the original members of the Common Market.

The paradox is striking. Once the Atlantic ocean so separated us from North America that the journey was fraught with dangers, the ships were inadequate for the cargoes that could be exchanged, vast areas of Canada were yet unknown, and her great wealth still undiscovered. In those days we traded freely. Now the journey is safe; there are ships, aircraft, railways and trucks to take our goods into every populated part of Canada, and to bring us what she can sell in exchange. Her immense resources are available to us. Nature's barriers have been pulled down. In their place are the politicians'. Maybe another generation will say it was something worse than a paradox. They might even liken it to economic warfare, because the effect, they may say, is much the same.

The case of Australia, in some ways, is even worse. Canada was part of a free trade area with the United States; the economies of both were interlocked, so either's loss was shared by the other. Australia had no such larger partner to lean upon.

When Mr Malcolm Fraser, then Prime Minister of Australia, spoke in the City of London a few years ago, he told his audience that one third of Australian dairy farmers had gone out of business as a direct result of our entry into the Common Market. He was trying to rebut the argument, made so often, that Australia had gained markets elsewhere and was now indifferent to ours. The fact is that our own domestic market is, without question, the most coveted of all for food exporters. Some of its advantages are shared with a few other countries, but none can claim them all. In the first place, everyone in Britain is assured of an income large enough to afford a reasonable amount of food. Secondly, more than three quarters of the British people live in cities and conurbations where it is easy to distribute food, and the remaining minority are mostly within reach of a supermarket. Thirdly, the transport of food from the ports to those points of distribution is quick and inexpensive compared with other countries. Fourthly, about nine tenths of British people buy most of their food from shops or supermarkets that themselves buy centrally, so that an exporter need make only a single contract to secure a nationwide outlet. Fifthly, the British people have no chauvinistic traditions when buying their food; on the contrary, many of them assume, for instance, that Danish bacon is better than our own. Sixthly, English is the language of international trade. A seventh reason why we are at an advantage may be peculiar to Australians and New Zealanders. Their roots are here and, if they cannot claim cousins to visit, they still come to London with special feelings. Every Australian concerned with the exporting of food would say, even now, that Britain would have first preference in his trade abroad – that is, if we allowed him to choose.

It is not quite so easy to see the effect on our exports to Australia, but any visitor will soon see and hear about the demise of our trade in manufactured goods. The British car, once ubiquitous, is now a rarity. Not even the staff of our own High Commission in Canberra seem particularly anxious to purchase our cars. Walking by its car park three years ago, I stopped to count how many of the thirty or so vehicles were of British origin; apart from what looked like the High Commissioner's Daimler, there was just one very elderly Morris. Most of the others were Continental, Renaults and Volkswagens and such like. Curiosity prompted me to go on later to the French Embassy. All the cars there were French!

To gain alternative markets to replace ours, the Australians have had to fight very hard. As often as not they have been defeated, and it has been the EEC that has usually defeated them. The main weapon used by the Community has been, of course, the export subsidy. The vast sums made available to it under the CAP have enabled it to undercut the prices of the Australians, while the revenue received by the Australian government could never have been large enough to allow it to retaliate. In Australia, as in the United States and Canada, agriculture is the first industry of the country and so her farmers are expected to support the government financially. Her other industries are neither rich nor numerous enough to carry the deadweight of a highly subsidised agriculture.

Australia has tried to diversify. Cotton, for example, can be grown in the place of wheat in parts of New South Wales, and this is being done. But diversification out of the crops which a country can grow most economically in conditions of fair competition seldom succeeds, because usually in some other part of the world the crop is already being grown to meet the existing demand. It has been the experience of Australian farmers that diversification is not, generally, a practical policy. So hundreds of thousands of acres capable of growing wheat at low cost now lie idle. Some have gone over to grass, but too little rainfall has prevented that from being a success.

One side of the agricultural depression in Australia can be illustrated anecdotally. On the occasion of my visit to Australia, I went up to Queensland to see at first hand the problems of the cane sugar growers. Most of the farms are about two hundred acres, the optimum size for one man to work by himself. Come the harvest, he is able to join with neighbours to bring in the cane of each farm in turn. They are highly mechanised and every farmer has become a specialist, for no other crop is grown in the area, where the soil and climate are ideal for the cane. By every conceivable yardstick, the whole industry, from the farms via the sugar factories to the sugar terminals, is highly efficient.

Yet visiting the farmers was not a happy experience. They have found it difficult to understand why we have specifically excluded their sugar from our market. I explained as best I could that it was not the wish of the British people, but the rules of the Common Market. Between 300,000 and 400,000 tonnes, which they had been exporting to us, had to find another market. The industry had been established to supply their domestic market and ours, and until 1972 we had in accordance with the Commonwealth Sugar Agreement been under contract to accept it. The agreement had worked considerably to our advantage, as it enabled us to eat sugar cheaper than anyone else, but not always to their advantage, because the terms of the contract prevented them from gaining the benefit of higher prices when the world supply fell short of world needs.

What upset me most of all in the visit was seeing the standard of living of these farmers, who had felt for so long a strong bond with what many of them still called 'home', though they may not have been born here nor even visited our shores. Linoleum on all the floors seemed universal, cheap wooden furniture, little if any modern equipment in the kitchen, and outside an elderly and dilapidated car. What I saw took me back to the thirties; it was just how our farmers lived then. Farm workers in my constituency are among the low paid and the minimum rate of pay (£79) usually prevails, but even their houses are more comfortable and up-to-date than those I saw in Queensland. I doubt if there is a single farmhouse in England, encircled by its two hundred acres, looking as poor as those I saw in Queensland; and if there is, it is the fault of its owner.

How they live in Queensland is the fault of the EEC in dumping onto the world market between one quarter and one fifth of its total supply at a price that may be half its cost of production. No matter how efficient they are in Queensland, that kind of competition cannot be endured. Our sugar policy has done so much damage elsewhere, especially to Third World countries whose economies depend upon being able to export sugar fairly, that the political and strategic consequences of what is happening are considered in the chapter on 'The Poorest Victims'.

New Zealand, too, has seen her agriculture go through a crisis. Like Australia's, her trade deficit has grown worse and tens of thousands of her farmers have become the poorer by what we have done. The fault is certainly not Nature's. Grass out there grows some ten or eleven months in the year – compared with six months with us – and vast flocks of sheep and great herds of cattle can eat all they need at low cost. They can, as a matter of hard fact, be fed cheaper in New Zealand than anywhere else in the world. When the 1,309 ton sailing ship, *Dunedin*, sailed into the port of London in 1882 with the first refrigerated shipment of meat and butter exported from New Zealand, it was the beginning of an enormous advantage to us in Britain. From then on we were to have preference over all others for the supply of all the butter, cheese and lamb that we might want, and every bit of it at the cheapest price in the world.

Some eighty per cent of New Zealand's exports were of food before we put up the barriers, and they are much the same today. She is still, as nature ordained her to be, a pastoral country, so she has had to search elsewhere for a market. Like the United States, Canada and Australia, she has had to compete against the dumped surpluses of the EEC, and although successful in some places, her food exports can no longer provide the degree of prosperity enjoyed by her people until we entered the EEC.

Fighting a trade war has cost New Zealand a great deal of money. Not only are her farmers individually the poorer in consequence, but also the government has been forced to divert expenditure to give them assistance. The same, of course, has gone for our other allies. In each case some part of the diversion has been from defence expenditure, and since Australia and New Zealand are of supreme strategic importance in the Southern Hemisphere, to weaken them is to weaken the Western alliance. It is one more example of the heavy indirect prices we are paying for the policies imposed on us over the last ten years.

6/The Poor Consumer

A generation ago we scarcely ever spoke of the 'consumer'. Now Consumer Councils have been set up, a Consumers' Association formed, newspaper columns are written about consumer affairs, radio and television programmes advise consumers, local authorities have Departments of Consumer Protection and, to top it all, there is a Minister for Consumer Protection. Unfortunately the consumer affairs industry has grown up behind – and a long way behind – the growth of protection of producers. The more we draft rules to help consumers, the more they are under attack by the government of the day. In a plain word, it is humbug.

The most effective protection the consumer can have is the freedom to choose. He himself decides what he should have, not some law-maker or civil servant. Thus he buys a banana instead of an orange because that is what he happens to want to eat though someone else might decree that an orange would be better for him or that it would be in the 'national interest' for him to buy it. This is not being fanciful, for we are induced to eat some kinds of food rather than others for that very reason. The bananas we eat are from either Jamaica or the Windward Islands, and only when their crops fail are we allowed to buy bananas from Ecuador and elsewhere.

Freedom to choose implies freedom to buy in one place rather than another. So far as most of us are concerned, it is the freedom to go to a supermarket or a market stall or an ordinary shop or any other place where the goods are honestly traded. It is, of course, a very obvious kind of freedom and we take it for granted. But we overlook how limited it can be in its effect. It becomes almost worthless if every shop and supermarket has the same kind of food on offer and sells it at the same price. The freedom to 'shop around' only has value when the retailers themselves can also shop around and give the customer a variety of choice. If all the bananas in all the retail outlets in the country came from the West Indies and they all sell at much the same price, the customer's freedom does not add up to anything worth having.

Protection is such a cosy, comforting word. The motive of the protector must be good; no doubt he is a kindly, well meaning sort. How difficult it is to criticise someone who wants to protect, and who assures us that British farmers must be protected. Indeed they must; but how and from whom? The protection they are now given is the wrong kind for two reasons. First, it fails in its objective, as the fourth chapter showed; secondly, the protection is against what the British people want. This should be a self-evident truth, for if the British people did not want to buy North American wheat, there would be no point in setting up an array of fiscal fences against it coming into our ports. If they did not want to buy butter from New Zealand, there would be no need for quota restrictions and levies. Because the British people would buy that wheat and butter if they had the freedom to do so, their freedom has to be curbed.

These simple truths get washed away in the flood of fine words about free trade heard at Mansion House dinners. No one stands up to say he is positively against free trade. More humbug! Protectionism is favoured by industries that think they will benefit from it, and the fact is that it is now rampant throughout the world: the officials in the office of General Agreement on Tariffs and Trade in Geneva, in making a survey of non-tariff barriers, concluded that there were forty-four categories of them.

For a nation to decide whether to adopt free trade or protectionism is really a question of will. Despite a nation's conscious determination to give the consumer his freedom, some protectionism may still lurk around in the form of a non-tariff barrier; and even in the heyday of free trade a century ago, a few such barriers existed. A few exceptions may not matter and little harm be done, provided the truth is acknowledged – that the freedom of the consumer is being curbed. The point is not as banal as it may seem. The interests that ask for protectionism – whether the NFU leadership or anyone else – and the powers that give it, in Westminster or Whitehall, never acknowledge the loss of freedom. Over the years there has been so much special pleading it seems to have blinded them to what should be obvious. Nor is it obvious to most of us. In this respect, people living in Eastern Europe have an advantage. Ration books are given out and every citizen knows that he cannot buy what he wants. The control over the British people is not so blatant, but it is there none the less, invisibly. Because Eastern Europeans know that their freedom of choice is curtailed and no politician can deny it, efforts are made to tell them why it is necessary. Here at home it is not so. We are allowed to pretend our freedom is unfettered as if intangible fetters are no fetters at all.

The chief method used to divert our decision is fiscal. The food we would prefer to eat is taxed. We are not aware how much we are taxed in this way, because we do not ourselves pay the tax directly to any agency of the government; it is passed on to us by the retailer, who has himself had the tax passed on to him by the wholesaler or importer. The more we would like to eat a food which the government does not want us to eat, the more heavily it is taxed, to the point when we are pushed into buying some other kind of food which the government does want us to buy. On some kinds of food the tax is so high that no one finds it worthwhile eating them any more, so that no retailer or wholesaler any longer trades in them. A considerable range of goods come into this category. Tinned salmon from Canada used to be on the table of hundreds of thousands of families twenty years ago, and it was so cheap that even poor families were able to enjoy it. Now there is an import duty on it. There are still plenty of salmon to be caught in Canada, and the tax is not imposed for any reason of conservation. The trouble with Canadian tinned salmon was that it was too cheap and too popular with the British people. They preferred it to the food produced in the Common Market.

Canada also used to send us great quantities of cheese and apples. The tax on Canadian cheddar is now 55 pence a pound, and that effectively doubles its price in the shops. Some people, it may be remembered, particularly liked it. Every quality grocer supplied it and many thousands of us bought it regularly, simply because we liked the taste.

Defenders of the present system will say that we can still have it if we must, but we should pay twice as much for it. Without trying to be too unkind, parked outside many a large-scale arable farmer's house is a diesel-driven Mercedes costing £15,000. Impose a duty on it which doubles the price, and the freedom to buy it becomes rather less real, for the obvious reason that sales would fall to a level at which importers would no longer find it profitable to hold the franchise. So with Canadian cheese, and the same can be said for many other kinds of food that used to be imported into our country. The instrument of taxation is used to keep them out of our shops; and in most cases it is to protect not our own producers but others in the Common Market.

Even the foods that are not entirely excluded from our market are almost all taxed to some degree. The exceptions are those foods which we do not want to eat in any quantity, usually those chosen by the ethnic minorities, like yams. The exceptions serve to emphasise that the more of a kind of imported food we want to eat, the more it is likely to be taxed.

So the fiscal weapon is used against the British people. Other weapons are also used. Quotas, prohibitions and the whole gamut of grants and subsidies are there to serve the same purpose. Of course, the government (I use the term in its wider sense of embracing all the institutions of the state) needs to curb our freedom in a lot of ways, but when it comes to controlling what we want to eat (need it be said, after breathing, the most essential of our activities?) the need to exercise that control should be proved. In plain words, we should eat what we like, unless it can be clearly shown that we ought not to do so. The burden of proof lies upon the government.

At long last, there is now broad agreement that these taxes have forced up the price of food for the British consumer. When I asserted in *Agriculture: The Triumph and the Shame* that they cost the consumer £3,000 millions a year (about £5 a week for a family of four) on top of the cost to the taxpayer (about another £2,000 millions) there were mutterings of disbelief in high places. In the debate that has followed, a consensus has emerged, and the figure of £3,000 is now accepted. The Institute of Fiscal Studies is of that opinion. So too is the Treasury. Mr Christopher Johnson, Group Economic Adviser to Lloyds Bank, prepared a detailed independent assessment which was published by the Centre for Agricultural Strategy and the Centre for European Agricultural Studies and his conclusion was the same. Even Mr Peter Walker, in one of the last statements he made as Minister of Agriculture, agreed! Writing in the *British Farmer and Stockbreeder* (4 January 1983) he admitted that a system of deficiency payments would cost £3,000 millions a year, which of course is really the same as saying that that is the difference between world prices and our own. Mr Robert Jackson in his booklet *From Boom to Bust?* chided me for a 'pervasive lack of contact with reality' and went on to concede that £3,000 millions was probably the right estimate. Yet on the very same page he said that the gross product of British agriculture was worth £5,420 millions. The awful significance of the extra burden upon the consumer being more than half agriculture's gross product passed him by; and when the Exchequer's costs and the actual net cost of food at the farmgate are added, the total cost becomes greater than the value of agriculture's gross product! The inference to be drawn, even from Mr Walker and Mr Jackson, amazing though it may seem, is that agriculture has reached such a high-cost level that we would be better off if our farmers produced no food at all. There is certainly a 'lack of contact with reality' somewhere!

£3,000 millions a year is enough to warrant the term 'poor consumers', for the British people are impoverished by that amount, having that much less to spend on other items they would have preferred to buy. Nor can it be dismissed as a trifling sum; it represents about one million motor cars, six million holidays in Spain, more than all the nation's rail fares and all we spend on clothes and furniture. By any reckoning, it is a massive diversion of consumer expenditure, and a serious loss of consumer welfare.

When prices go up we have to buy rather less than we would otherwise have done, and with food our pattern of consumption changes: we tend to eat food of a lower quality. The following

Table, compiled from the National Food Survey, illustrates what has happened to the poor consumer of Britain since the import taxes began.

Average Weekly Consumption of Main Foods
(in ounces unless stated otherwise)

	1971	1981	Percentage change
Milk	4·46 pints	3·94 pints	–13·2
Beef	7·96	6·96	–12·6
Mutton and Lamb	5·41	4·25	–21·0
Bacon and Ham	5·12	4·14	–19·1
Butter	5·53	3·69	–33·2
Sugar	15·80	11·08	–28·9
Eggs	4·66	3·68	–21·0

Mr Teddy Taylor asked in the House of Commons what was the import levy on those items. According to the Written Answer (*Hansard*, 1 November 1983, columns 341 and 342), the import levy on beef worked out at 96 pence a pound; on mutton and lamb there is a special levy of 10 per cent of c.i.f. value but imports are limited by what is euphemistically called a 'Voluntary Restraint Agreement'; the import levy on bacon is 21·9 pence a pound, on butter it is 61 pence a pound, on sugar 10·7 pence a pound and eggs, 30 pence a pound.

With taxes so high it may be obvious why in a little more than a decade our eating habits have undergone a major change. It might be said that, being more conscious of our health, we are buying less butter and sugar, but doctors make no accusations about the other items. Common sense suggests that a tax of 96 pence a pound on beef is the reason why we are eating 12 per cent less. The truth of the matter is known in every household: we are eating differently and it is not because we wish to do so. Of course, habits change over the years, but (except in wartime) there has not been a time when the diet of the British people has altered so quickly as it has these last ten years.

The taxing of food strikes at everyone, no matter how low their income may be. The poorest in the land, no more than the millionaire, can escape the net. The difference is, of course, that while the millionaire might not feel the pinch, the poorest men and women find themselves carrying a particularly heavy burden. A family of four living on social security will probably have an income of less than £70 a week. For them £5 is an important sum, and the bitter irony is that the farmworker who is supposed to benefit may be no better off. In my own constituency there are several thousand farm workers on low pay and there is seldom much difference in income for many of them whether working or not. A farm worker with four children is often better off financially when he loses his job.

When I first became the MP for Holland-with-Boston, I was appalled at the low wages received by the employees on the farms in that part of Lincolnshire, substantially less than what I or my neighbours paid in Berkshire. Whenever I mentioned it the answer was always much the same: 'We would like to pay higher wages to our men: we could if we had higher returns.' We have introduced a system of 'protecting' farm workers whose real effect is to tax them five to ten per cent of their income. Precisely the same argument as the agricultural lobby uses today was raised a hundred and fifty years ago to justify opposition to the repeal of the Corn Laws: take away protection and there will be widespread poverty in the countryside. Then the farm worker's income was ten shillings a week, of which five shillings went on food and most of that on bread. Once the Corn Laws were repealed, the proportion of his income that went on bread fell considerably and his standard of living rose accordingly. The same would happen today.

A cynic may claim that nowadays any mischief is made good by the Family Income Supplement and higher rates of social security benefit. That is true for many families, but not for those whose self-respect demands that they should have a job despite its low pay, rather than 'live off the state'. Besides, it scarcely helps the nation's economy if the huge cost of social security is inflated by paying out more than should be necessary. In 1983, the government spent some £17,000 millions on the various forms of social security. A free trade policy would enable that massive sum to be reduced by not less than £1,000 millions, so that other forms of taxation could also be cut by that amount.

Quite astonishing examples of special pleading have come from the people who defend the policy of taxing food, and they usually lace it with a judicious selection of statistics. Here is one:

It remains a fact that food is continually becoming cheaper for the British consumer in real terms. Between 1977 and 1982 non-food prices in Britain went up by an average of 12·7 per cent a year; average earnings went up by 14·3 per cent; and food prices by only 9·5 per cent. Prices received by farmers went up by even less – 7·1 per cent a year.

It was in a letter published in the correspondence column of the *Daily Telegraph* and signed by Mr Richard Maslen, the Director of Information at the National Farmers' Union. In the field of statistics there cannot be any rule more elementary than that one should compare like with like, and another elementary rule is that when making comparisons between one policy and another, one should take as one's base year the time when a change of policy took place. There was no change of policy whatsoever in 1977 – it just happens to be a convenient year for a special pleader to adopt, as it was after a period when prices had risen sharply. The proper year to select for one's base is the last full year before we went over to the system of import levies, 1971.

Next, the figures he quotes as 'average earnings' are those for industrial earnings, as if industrial workers and British consumers were one and the same. In fact, they represent a minority of consumers. When millions of people are out of work and we have the largest-ever proportion of our population retired, besides a record number of people in full-time education, the proper comparison is not between earnings in any two years, but incomes generally, including also pensions.

Thirdly, Mr Maslen includes all food prices; but tropical foods, such as bananas, coffee, tea etc. have gone down in price in real terms for reasons given in a subsequent chapter. For Mr Maslen to take credit for the depressed prices of food grown in the Third World is, as the saying goes, 'a bit rich'. The proper comparison is with the food grown in our own country.

Now let us take those three different criteria, and see how the NFU argument looks. Between 1971 and 1980 (the latest year for which figures are available) incomes went up by 344 per cent, an average of 14·7 per cent. Home grown food prices rose by 472 per cent, an average of 18·8 per cent. Farm incomes went up from 1971 to 1982 by 181·5 per cent, an average of 5·5 per cent. That last figure includes all farmers. If we look at the incomes of arable farmers (the real beneficiaries) and if we accept Mr Maslen's base year of 1977, we find that in the five years up to 1982 they doubled! So the true story is very different from the one the NFU would like us to believe.

Artificially high prices for consumers also put up the high-input/high-output ratio. Because the retail shops, and especially the supermarkets, want to maintain their sales of food, they have passed the signal down the chain of supply that food costs must be lowered. The farmer, at the end of the chain, is forced to respond by increasing his output. Being hooked on a high-input/high-output system he has, therefore, to increase his inputs still further to gain the extra production. At the same time the world of agricultural research is at hand (with £140 millions of public money) to advise him on new and more intensive inputs, if not costlier in money terms, at least costlier to the environment and probably to our health.

Let us take a few examples of the ways in which this affects the poor consumer. As we saw, the system of grants and tax allowances favours the intensive methods of keeping livestock to the prejudice of extensive ones, and on top of that the artificially high price of farmland adds to the handicap. The result is that more and more pigs are kept in the same sized pens, more and more cows in the same dairy, and if it is at all possible to squeeze another hen into the battery cage, the deed is done. Increasing the density brings the inevitable hazard of disease, and as it increases, so also does the use of drugs. Inordinate quantities of antibiotics are today being bought by the intensive producer. The Swann Committee's Report was disturbing enough. Now what most doctors were suspecting is accepted, that by eating meat impregnated with antibiotics we become immune to their effect when we ourselves are in need of them.

Stock also have to be induced to grow quicker. A pork or bacon pig can be ready for slaughter several weeks sooner today than was the case twenty-five years ago; and as he may eat three or four pounds of expensive food every day of his later life, the sooner he is large enough to send to the slaughterhouse, the better. Hence a range of growth stimulants may be administered. Arsenic is one, in tiny doses; and hormones; and copper. Growth stimulants could, by their very nature, be carcinogenic, and while it may be safe to brush aside our doubts, some doctors are worried at the way the use of these growth stimulants is increasing.

One kind of meat should be safe to eat – beef. Beef cattle used to be raised mainly on our pastures, fed on grass in the growing seasons and hay in the winter. It was low-cost, but a lot of land was needed for it. Our famous beef cattle, such as Herefords and Aberdeen Angus, gave us top quality meat. The cow's period of gestation is nine months, so each cow can give birth to a calf a year and rear it herself on her own milk, and three months later be ready to be served again. One cow, one calf is the principle of single suckling. If the calf is born in the spring, it has a flying start in life, and the blend of plenty of milk and summer grass is a certain way to rear a healthy beef animal. The herds of Herefords and others were kept out of doors all the year, the grass in the summer and the hay in the winter being their diet. Their growth was not hurried, and if they took two and a half years to reach the desired weight, their meat tasted all the better for it.

It was an example of low-cost farming; the total cost of inputs of fertiliser, pesticides, housing and bought-in feed compounds was nothing; the input of labour not very much. But the profitability of the system depended upon the price of pasture land reflecting its natural economic value. With its actual price today perhaps £2,000 an acre, producing this top quality beef is no longer as profitable as it ought to be, even with a stocking rate of one cow to the acre. So we resort to various ways to increase our 'productivity' or our 'efficiency'. Why keep your beef herds out in open fields when with a slight adjustment you can keep them indoors all the year round in grant-aided, tax-deductible buildings and plough up the pastures to grow wheat at £140 a tonne? That, of course, is what has happened; but Herefords, Aberdeen Angus, North Devons, Sussex, Shorthorns and all the other true beef animals do not respond to being kept indoors all the time. It is true that some breeders do not act like this (myself included), but only because sheer profit is not their paramount concern. Some, I know, carry on in the hope that the policy makers will change the system. For the most part, other kinds of beef animals are used. Calves from the dairy herds are obvious candidates, as they have always been, and most of our beef comes from them anyway. Cattle from abroad have been imported, especially from France and Switzerland, which respond more readily to more hurried methods and which fatten faster with feed compounds. It is noticeable that Charolais and Charolais crosses as well as the Simmental and Limousin are much fussier feeders than our native cattle; they leave alone the rougher pasture and because it is left alone by them, it gets rougher still, so a field of permanent pasture deteriorates with them and soon comes to need ploughing up and reseeding with modern grasses. With the plough is lost lots of flora which have qualities which do seem to be good for the health and well-being of our cattle. Meadowsweet is one of them, but there are many others that an older generation of stockmen believed acted as tonics, nature's way of keeping her animals fit. Herbalists, of course, insist they are good for humans too, and are remedies for a variety of our maladies.

The poor consumer need not agree with herbalism to realise that this new way of rearing beef is questionable. The butchers themselves, through the National Federation of Meat Traders, have said in the plainest terms that the quality of our beef is going down rapidly. The Federation represents butchers generally, but particularly the smaller firms and family butchers, who have always tried to provide meat of good quality, often being in a position to advise the housewife how to cook a particular joint and take an interest in the eating of it as well as the selling. The family butchers are convinced that unless they can serve their customers with quality their days may be numbered; but how can they do so when the taxpayer is subsidising farmers to produce the opposite?

Not only are the imported beef breeds and the by-products of our dairy herds intrinsically of poorer quality (as the pages of the *Meat Trader* assure us to be the case). Their method of being reared also diminishes the quality of the meat. When they are kept indoors, especially with a high stocking density, antibiotics may have to be brought into use, as they are with pigs. The animals are fed a richer diet of feed compounds that are intended to quicken their growth, and though the result is claimed to be lean meat ('what the housewife wants'), the truth is that there is likely to be more fat within the 'eye' of the meat, the fat being diffused in what appears to be lean meat, instead of reaching the outside of the carcass where it can be cut off easily either in the butcher's shop or in the kitchen or on the dinner plate itself.

The reseeded fields on which these animals feed (in so far as they go into a field) have a limited number of grasses, and these have to be treated with a range of fertilisers and herbicides. The fertilisers are likely to be phosphates and nitrates. Studies have been made into the effect an excess of phosphates may be having upon us, but as they have been in West Germany and the United States they have had little publicity over here. Research in both countries suggests that there has been a considerable increase in phosphate in a number of important food products, red meat and dairy products particularly, and more than a certain quantity can have an adverse effect on the central nervous system. (The University of Mainz Clinic advises that children prone to be hyperactive should be given a diet low in phosphates.) Plainly we have much to learn in this area, and even if the research so far undertaken is qualified in the future we must realise that the existing high-input/high-output system is steadily increasing the quantity of phosphate being applied to our soil.

The evidence about nitrates is clearer. As I write this, an official report on the effect nitrates are having on our water supply is being prepared. Leaks about its contents hint that it will have some serious words to say. It seems that the levels of nitrates (or nitrites as a result of nitrates interacting) are rising fast and that the water supply from many of our rivers will be seriously polluted by the standards of the World Health Organisation. Nitrates have been widely used by arable farms and dairy farms as well as beef producers (in fact nearly all our agricultural land is receiving heavier doses of nitrates as every year goes by).

That is not the end of the matter for the poor consumer. There are some 3,500 additives to our food today, and they join our diet at any time from the moment the seed enters the soil to when it leaves some factory or processing plant on the last leg of its journey to the shop. Perhaps all of them are wholly safe; perhaps none of them can harm any of us. Yet, as doctors say, what is harmless to most of us may be harmful to some, and what may not harm one part of someone's anatomy may harm another part of someone else's. We have different target areas in our bodies, some more vulnerable than others. With one man it is his heart, with his brother, it is his central nervous system, and with the third brother it is neither. What doctors are certain about is that the central nervous system seems more fragile than it used to be, and more ailments and disorders appear to stem from neurological causes.

Doctors are less sure about allergies. Some time ago I was persuaded to attend a conference on this subject for doctors, school teachers, magistrates, social workers and others, where the connection between allergies and criminal or antisocial behaviour was discussed. The doctor who gave the principal paper to the conference, made the bold assertion that some, though far from all, cases of depression and schizophrenia could be attributed to food additives attacking the central nervous system He had been engaged to treat private patients in our mental hospitals who were detained because of those two disorders, and he had been able to secure their release because he had found that when these patients gave up eating certain foodstuffs, their mental illness was cured. Another point made at the conference was that milk is increasingly an allergen. Of course, one cannot go far as to say that the high inputs of dairy farming are the reason for this, but to rule out the possibility altogether and to claim with total confidence that modern farming practices are having no adverse effect upon anyone's health, may be taking optimism one step further than we should. One of the circumstances in which the nation is entitled, through its legislators, to interfere with the farmer as a businessman is to protect its health. It may be too early to speak of specific controls and prohibitions; yet it cannot be too early to promote research into this field. Instead of the government spending £140 millions on research designed to achieve more output, public money should go into probing some of these inputs.

If those moral and economic considerations are not

compelling evidence against protectionism, the political effect upon the consumer's interest should make it conclusive. Once a policy of free trade gives way to protectionism, power begins to pass from the consumer to the producer in a number of ways that are difficult to discern. Free trade exists naturally: it is a fact of commerce unless and until a government intervenes to restrict the freedom of the individual to buy what he wants. As soon as a government begins to impose restrictions, even with the best of motives, it is taking the side of the producer against the consumer.

No word may be said that the consumer is to be prejudiced; on the contrary, protectionist measures are always couched in terms that suggest the opposite. What is important is that the producer is made aware that he is to be helped. The thin end of the wedge has been inserted. It is at this point that producers find it in their interests to associate together and speak to the government with a united voice. A little protection leads to a request for more; and there is never a stage when those protected sit back in a state of contentment. The present-day lobbying by the NFU illustrates it only too well. Despite all the massive help given to agriculture (and it has been insidiously increasing year by year for over half a century) the NFU is far from satisfied. Not a single day goes by – as the NFU admits – without it making some representation to the Ministry of Agriculture or the Treasury or some other Department for still more help.

The day I write this (20 January 1984) an article in *Farmers' Weekly*, after describing more conventional forms of lobbying, tells us:

. . . there is the more undercover style of lobbying which the NFU does so well. This means knowing who the most powerful people are on a certain issue and bringing them round to the farmers' point of view. It is the kind of lobbying which goes on at lunchtimes, in bars and at private dinner parties where Cabinet Ministers are mellowed by good claret and port. It's expensive and exclusive, but it works. . .

Ask one of the NFU staff men who unashamedly revel in their ability to play the game – or manipulate others into playing it – whether the system is just, and he will just shrug his shoulders. It's the way the world goes round.

Of course the NFU is not alone in this respect. The list of associations concerned with food or agriculture whose purpose in some way is to extend the empire of protectionism steadily gets longer. Here are sixty-seven of them, most of them formed in recent years. Note where in London their offices are.

Agricultural Engineers Association
   6 Buckingham Gate, SW1.
Agricultural Lime Producers Council
   14 Waterloo Place, SW1.
Agricultural Research Council
   160 Great Portland Street, W1.
Association of Agriculture
   16-20 Strutton Grove, SW1.
Association of Tinned Cream Manufacturers
   20 Eastbourne Terrace, W2.
Association of Manufacturers and Exporters of Concentrated and Unconcentrated Soft Drinks
   1-2 Castle Lane, SW1.
Association of British Abattoir Owners
   5 Charterhouse Square, EC1.
Association of British Manufacturers of Milk Powder
   Brettenham House, Lancaster Gate, W2.
Association of British Pharmaceutical Industry
   162 Regent Street, W1.
Association of Butter Blenders and Butter and Cheese Packers
   20 Eastbourne Terrace, W2.
British Agriculture Export Council
   35 Belgrave Square, SW1.
British Agrochemicals Association
   93 Albert Embankment, SE1.
British Farm Produce Council
   25 Knightsbridge, SW1.
British Poultry Meat Association
   52-54 High Holborn, WC1.
British Poultry Breeders and Hatcheries Association
   52-54 High Holborn, WC1.
British Poultry Federation
   52-54 High Holborn, WC1.

British Soft Drinks Council
    6 Catherine Street, SW1.
British Seeds Council
    25 Knightsbridge, SW1.
British Sugar Bureau
    140 Park Lane, W1.
British Oatmeal Millers Association
    6 Catherine Street, WC2.
British Hay and Straw Merchants Association
    70 Wigmore Street, W1.
British Egg Association
    52-54 High Holborn, WC1.
British Turkey Federation
    52-54 High Holborn, WC1.
Bacon and Meat Manufacturers Association
    6 Catherine Street, WC2.
British Pest Control Association
    93 Albert Embankment, SE1.
Bakery Allied Trades Association
    6 Catherine Street, WC2.
Central Council for Agricultural and Horticultural Cooperation
    19 Elm Lane, SW8.
Cookery and Food Association
    324 Grays Inn Road, WC2.
Country Landowners Association
    16 Belgrave Square, SW1.
Chemical Industries Association
    93 Albert Embankment, SE1.
Cake and Biscuit Alliance
    127-131 Regent Street, W1.
Dairy Trade Federation
    20 Eastbourne Terrace, W2.
Delicatessen and Fine Foods Association
    21 Park Square East, NW1.
Duck Producers Association
    52-54 High Holborn, WC1.
Farm Management Association
    Parker Street, WC2.

Federation of Agricultural Cooperatives
    25 Knightsbridge, SW1.

Fruit Traders Federation
    8-15 Russell Chambers, WC2.

Food and Drink Industries Council
    25 Victoria Street, SW1.

Food Freezer and Refrigerator Council
    25 North Row, W1.

Food Manufacturers Association
    6 Catherine Street, WC2.

Food Manufacturers Industrial Group
    6 Catherine Street, WC2.

Frozen Food Producers Association
    1 Green Street, W1.

Fruit and Vegetable Canners Association
    6 Catherine Street, WC2.

Fertiliser Manufacturers Association
    93 Albert Embankment, SE1.

Fertiliser Society
    93 Albert Embankment, SE1.

Grain and Feed Trade Association
    28 St. Mary Axe, EC3.

Institute of Corn and Agricultural Merchants
    3 Whitehall Court, SW1.

International Wheat Council
    28 Haymarket, SW1.

International Wool Secretariat
    6 Carlton Gardens, SW1.

Multiple Food and Drink Retailers Association
    1-19 New Oxford Street, WC1.

Multiple Food Retailers Employers Association
    1-19 New Oxford Street, WC1.

National Council of Concentrate Manufacturers
    7 Parkside, SW1.

National Dairy Centre
    5-7 John Princes Street, W1.

National Association of Tripedressers
    20-21 Princes Street, W1.

National Dairy Herds Association
103 Kingsway, WC2.

National Dairymens Association
20 Eastbourne Terrace, W2.

National Edible Oils Distributors Association
6 Catherine Street, WC2.

National Egg Packers Association
1 London Bridge, SE1.

National Association of Creamery Proprietors and Wholesale Dairymen
20 Eastbourne Terrace, W2.

National Association of Soft Drinks Manufacturers
50 Alexandra Road, SW19.

National Federation of Wholesale Grocers and Provision Merchants
18 Fleet Street, EC4.

Royal Association of British Dairy Farmers
Robarts House, Rossmore Road, NW1

Retail Fruit Trade Federation
8-15 Russel Chambers, WC2.

Take Away Food Federation
34 John Adam Street, WC2.

UK Association of Frozen Food Producers
1 Green Street, W1.

UK Agricultural Supply Trade Association
3 Whitehall Court, SW1.

Vegetable Protein Association
1-2 Castle Lane, SW1.

Some of them may not behave like the NFU and may never pour the best claret down the throats of the Cabinet. But what draws them, like bluebottles to a cowpat, to the most costly part of the Kingdom? Drawn they have been, for many of them once had offices far away, in places like Birmingham or Bedford which were geographically closer to their members. Perhaps the move is to suit their interests rather than their convenience. The offices are where they are, despite the high rents and rates, because for most of them it is functionally necessary for them to be near Westminster and Whitehall. So each one is within striking distance of 'where the action is'. It indicates their primary purpose – to influence the government so that it will interfere in such a way as to assist their members. To give this help without injuring either the taxpayer or the consumer may be possible, but a few moments' reflection ought to make us realise that help of that kind is likely to be trivial or peripheral.

When a producers' association asks the government for some form of assistance it is one of three kinds: advice, money or regulation. Advice, in itself, may cost the taxpayer no more than the time of some politician or civil servant over a cup of tea. A tiny expense, but how often will it end with mere advice? Besides, there is little advice that either of them can give to the producers' association unless it relates to public money or public control. These two kinds of assistance are inroads either into the pocket of the taxpayer or the freedom of the consumer. We can be sure that when a producers' association approaches a branch of government it is to ask it to 'do' something. Now there is one truth about all governments that is certain – they can only 'do' something for us by taking away either our money or our freedom. As often as not, they take both. Whenever the government decides to spend more money in any field of expenditure, by even the smallest amount, without spending less in another field, it must take that money away from all the people in the form of inflation or from some of the people by taxation. Freedom of choice and purchasing power go hand in hand. The more purchasing power is entrusted to the government, the less freedom is left to the consumer to buy what he chooses – and this is particularly true if the consumer is a poor family which has little money over after buying essentials.

Of course, the scores of producers' associations that beaver away in the environs of government do not see themselves in that light. Most of them would be deeply hurt if they were told that they were making inroads on the consumer's freedom of choice, but simple logic makes it difficult to draw any other inference from what they are doing.

Let us explore the methods they use to influence the government. Not much harm may be done when the chairman of the producers' association takes a deputation to see an official or a Minister to urge him to consider some change of policy. No, nor is much achieved either when that is the only step taken by the association. Every government department receives so many representations from outside bodies that merely making a point across a table is seldom enough to secure a change of direction. The consequence is that all these associations know that to get their way much more needs to be done. Long before any direct move is made, it is wise to get on good terms with the Minister and his top officials; and the engagement for luncheon or dinner has become the accepted means to that end.

An incoming Minister will receive plenty of invitations. Mr John Silkin tells the story that as soon as he was appointed Minister of Agriculture a letter came in addressed to 'Dear John'. It was from the President of NFU, until then a total stranger to him, but the familiar approach was presumably intended to begin a nice, friendly relationship. The first task of the producer associations is to get themselves on good terms with their counterparts in the government departments. Having been a member of the Select Committee on Agriculture for some years I have seen many of them come before us as witnesses. And I have seen the same faces in the Reform Club together with Ministry officials or members of the public relations business, a large part of which serves also the business of lobbying. 'There is no such thing as a free lunch,' I say to myself as I pass by their table.

Who is paying for the lunch? The lobbyist pays the actual bill; he passes on the cost to the association; the association passes it on to its members; and the members pass it on to – inevitably – the consumer. But the price of the lunch, of course, goes far beyond the cost of the meal. It ends, or is intended to end, with a decision in favour of the lobbyist. And that decision is unlikely to be in favour of the consumer.

In these proceedings Parliament is not left out. The lobbyists may try to influence individual MPs, knowing that they can exert pressure upon a Minister to coincide with their own direct approaches (though, as we saw in Chapter 1, the NFU itself is beginning to take MPs for granted.) Nor are journalists excluded. The modern reporter in this field does not have to go out of Fleet Street to get his stories, and the newspaper proprietors, always conscious of rising costs, are only too glad to allow outside sources to feed in news items. Each newspaper has the opportunity of receiving the same information. The facts themselves are sure to be correct, but like a brief to a barrister, they are not intended to be an objective assessment of the whole matter. They are what the producers' association would wish the reader to digest, and though there may be occasions when the two are the same, it is probable that they will be quite different. Why, after all, should the producers' association want to influence the press in the first place? If its object is to change government policy by getting a Minister's decision in favour of its members, the newspaper reader's interest, as a consumer, is almost sure to be prejudiced; and if the object is something different there appears to be little purpose in the association spending its time and money on feeding the press with its information.

At stake is 'big money'. Agriculture is itself big money. ICI reports that its income from its agricultural division is now £1,350 millions, and the whole edifice of farm support buttresses a number of great companies more than the farmers themselves. Some of them act as their own producers' association. They wine and dine Ministers, MPs, civil servants and journalists as assiduously as the associations, and they do so for exactly the same purpose.

The interest of the consumer does not end with the price he has to pay. A question mark must be put against the way some of the herbicides, pesticides and other poisonous chemicals have been allowed to be sold in our country. Elsewhere, the sale of a poison like 245T is forbidden by law on the simple ground that the evidence of its danger to both humans and the environment generally is too great. The market for the sale of hormone-based weed killers is immense, millions of pounds a year, and if the Ministry of Agriculture were to form the same opinion about their dangers as its counterparts in other countries, the companies that make and sell these extremely toxic chemicals would stand to lose a great deal of money. The amount of research required to be done by these companies is not as extensive as it is in other countries, and a cynic may suggest that the companies will try to persuade the Ministry that it is unnecessary for us to adopt the higher standards that prevail elsewhere. Those doubts are hardened when the

Ministry refuses to reveal the nature of the tests.

Little of this can be known to the poor consumer. Girls in the office who make the engagements, and waiters as they serve the lobster, may have an idea of what it is about, but as poor consumers themselves, do they appreciate how their own interests are being interfered with?

The process of lobbying does not stand still. Within it are forces that propel it on its way trying to get even more out of the system. No producers' association, whether the NFU, CLA or any other, will one day declare to its members that its role is over and its work done. It would mean every office holder and official declaring himself redundant. It would be as if Arthur Scargill were to announce that the NUM had served its purpose and that he could now return to work at the coal face, and his Daimler car and all the other assets of the NUM could be sold and the proceeds given back to the members, who no longer needed a union.

Far from producers' associations being dissolved, their number steadily increases. Government intervention makes them necessary; protectionism breeds them. Journalists weary of Fleet Street or politicians defeated at the polls have not been backward in filling in the gaps and suggesting to various groups how their interests can be looked after by them. After all, it is quite an agreeable job to have, and there is a lot one can do with the expense account.

The only possible way to reverse this tendency is for the government to begin the process of disengagement – in plain words to stop interfering with the consumer's freedom of choice. Sadly, it is a tall order, for governments thrive on power. The pursuit of power is the motor that moves nearly every politician and nearly every administrative official and to give power back to the consumer would entail giving up what they would prefer to keep.

None of this lobbying against the consumer was possible in those decades when we enjoyed a free trade policy. True, guilds and associations existed, but their functions were different, being chiefly the training of apprentices and the maintaining of standards. Some of them did restrict trade, but there was a necessary concern for the consumer's welfare, born out of self interest, for unless they did look after the welfare of the consumer as well as their own, free trade enabled competition from across the seas to put matters right.

Those were the days when there were no free lunches. That age has passed away to become an historical memory. Not until we enjoy the same principles of free trade will our interests be properly guarded again. Until then we remain the poor consumers.

7/Two Million Unemployed

The high degree of agricultural protectionism that we have had for many years, overlaid by the CAP, may seem an unlikely cause of millions being made out of work. There are six reasons why it is so. Before coming to them, let us take a glance at the size of our problem of unemployment and the outlook for the future, and also look at the other causes put forward to see how valid they may be.

Perhaps the size of our problem is best seen by comparing it with other countries. Full employment is usually taken to be when 2 per cent or less of a nation is out of work. Today, 12 per cent of the British people are registered unemployed. Many thousands of others, particularly married women, would seek a job were there hope of getting one; and a further two or three hundred thousand others would be added to the unemployed but for the various job creation and early retirement schemes that have been brought in. Economically speaking, the true total of unemployed must be nearly four millions. Even the registered number is more than it was in the darkest years before the War (and it might be added, those were the days when the Civil Service and local government had not mopped up between them a further two million men and women).

The rate of unemployment in France is 8 per cent, so if our rate was the same as the French, the number of British people out of work would be about a million less than it is. The comparison with Germany is worse; there the rate is 6 per cent, and such a rate would reduce our unemployment by two million. The rate among the smaller countries in the Common Market appears to be appreciably worse than the larger ones, but with an average which is less than ours. The figures quoted come from the OECD, and they also give the rates for other western European countries that have decided to remain outside the EEC. It may be significant that they do not seem to be afflicted with any problem of unemployment. In Switzerland the rate is 0·8 per cent, in Norway 2·0 per cent, in Sweden 3·0 per cent and in Austria 4·0 per cent. The OECD has also reported on the comparative wealth of its member countries on the basis of gross national product per head of the population. Of the top ten countries, five are western European countries who have indicated that they do not wish to join the EEC, led by Switzerland and Norway.

Nor does the outlook for the future give us much hope. The Cambridge Economic Policy Group suggests that we are likely to have an increasing number of unemployed, five million or even more. While others may be less dismal, no one points to any hard and firm evidence that the number will go down in the next few years.

In the search for explanations, one favourite is the familiar bogey of monetarism. Yet the Government's decision to keep the increase in the money supply broadly in line with the growth of our gross domestic product is in keeping with what Germany has been doing for many years, and to blame monetary policy for our unemployment is difficult to reconcile with the German experience. Nor does it account for the south-east of England being largely unscathed.

That the rest of the United Kingdom is suffering so much more goes some way to confirm one particular danger of our membership of the EEC in its present form. A number of distinguished economists have maintained throughout all the debates on the subject, from the very beginning, that being outside the hub and nave of the Common Market – the growth point in the middle – these areas would suffer a recession and large-scale unemployment as our own national economy became merged into that of the rest of the Community. No industrialist is likely to set up a new enterprise or expand an existing one on the periphery of the market. It is the first of the reasons why unemployment is so much worse than in other countries, and it certainly commends itself to common sense.

It is sometimes spoken of as the 'golden hub' or 'golden triangle' argument, the triangle being the area formed within Paris, Hamburg and Milan where the main industrial growth is to be found. It compares with the middle parts of England in the last century when a common market of the four countries of the British Isles came into being, and the industrial revolution was followed by a railway system, the two together giving us an integrated economy. Hundreds of thousands of Irish, Welsh and Scots moved into the middle parts of England, the golden hub of the United Kingdom, to share in the prosperity. They left behind depressed areas. The periphery was no place for an industrialist to go.

Similar thoughts, it seems, have prompted the leaders of many of our largest companies in the last ten years in deciding to invest their capital in the golden hub of today's Common Market. Very many millions of pounds are involved, and by setting up new plants and factories over there, they have created jobs for many tens of thousands of Frenchmen, Germans and others.

A notable example is ICI. They have put up plants in this golden area to produce plastics, paints and pharmaceuticals, and recruited eleven thousand workers. Their investment runs into hundreds of millions of pounds and now no less than half their sales to Western Europe are produced over there – about £700,000,000 worth a year. The case of ICI is interesting because no company has done more to raise money for the campaign to persuade the British people to support membership of the Common Market. The first fund-raising for the European Movement was done in their boardroom, and when the Referendum came, the company released a prominent member of their staff to help run the campaign with the slogan 'Out of Europe, Out of Work'. At the very time that they made the largest contribution to the campaign to persuade the British people that they would lose their jobs unless they voted 'Yes', it is now known that they were planning to invest many millions of pounds to export jobs from this country to France, Germany and Italy. Rowntree Macintosh Ltd gave a more modest contribution to the campaign to scare the British people about unemployment, only £10,000, and its directors forthwith put up a factory in Hamburg to supply our market as well as the Continent with sweets. The European Movement is shy about giving any information about the source of its funds, even to its members, but enough is now known to confirm what a cynic might assume. The list of British industrial companies that have given it money is much the same as the list of British industrial companies that have chosen to invest and expand in the golden hub of the Common Market, instead of in Britain.

The decision by all these companies to manufacture in the golden hub is obviously one of the reasons why our trade with the rest of the Common Market in manufactured goods has changed with such dramatic speed. The drama is a tragedy for the many thousands who have lost their jobs.

The following Table tells the sorry story. It comes from a Written Answer given to Mr Teddy Taylor and is to be found in *Hansard* for 19 January 1984, columns 297 and 298.

United Kingdom Trade in Manufactures to the European Community* (£ million)

	Exports	Imports	Visible Balance
1970	1,962	1,431	+531
1971	2,059	1,728	+331
1972	2,281	2,331	–50
1973	3,015	3,481	–466
1974	4,330	4,965	–635
1975	4,699	5,408	–709
1976	6,773	7,441	–668
1977	8,672	9,424	–752
1978	9,704	11,510	–1,806
1979	12,031	14,585	–2,554
1980	13,285	14,446	–1,161
1981	12,518	15,087	–2,569
1982	13,718	18,059	–4,341
Jan-Sept 1983	10,961	16,215	–5,254

* present membership throughout

Fortunately, our trade with countries outside the EEC is much better and shows a surplus, but our total trade in manufactured goods is now worse than it has been for centuries. Indeed, it is an extraordinary fact that for the first time since the reign of Henry VIII, we import more manufactured goods than we export! Another dismal fact is that our manufacturing output is now 10 per cent lower than it was in the year we joined the Common Market, and this represents a fall comparable to that between 1929 and 1933. Again, it is useful to compare this fall in output with an increase for France and Germany. French manufacturing output is up 12 per cent compared with 1975 (they have no records before then) and Germany's is up 13 per cent. The source for these startling figures is *Main Economic Indicators*, January 1984 and *Historical Statistics*, 1960-1979.

Several comments can be made about the figures in the Table. For a long period of time we succeeded in exporting more manufactured goods to the rest of the EEC than they exported to us. Then the position changed, and the change came at the very time we entered the Common Market. The longer we remain inside, the worse the balance of trade in manufactured goods appears to be. A deficit at the rate of £7,000,000,000 a year must represent a large number of jobs. Economists are generally agreed that it is not less than a million.

This decline in our manufacturing industry has been brought about, it is sometimes said, by a strike-happy workforce, obsessed with restrictive practices, lengthy tea breaks and other heinous matters. It may be a reason why the Ford Motor Company and British Leyland have both put up new plant on the Continent, but the other companies, like ICI, that have invested so heavily over there have on the whole had good industrial relations in this country. Besides, our manufacturing industries have a strike record generally no worse than that prevailing in France, Germany or Italy. In the last ten years there has been a sharp fall in the number of strikes in the private sector, and they are a small fraction of the number that used to take place. In fact, working days lost by various forms of industrial action in the private sector are almost insignificant, and absenteeism is also much reduced, so it seems contrary to the evidence to suggest that the British people are worse employees than those who are fortunate enough to be in the golden hub.

The explanation that we have 'priced ourselves out of the market' cannot be totally true because we are successfully selling our manufactured goods to countries outside the Common Market as we were in 1970. This is shown in the following Table, which formed part of the same Written Answer that Mr Teddy Taylor received on 19 January 1984.

United Kingdom Trade in Manufactures to non-EEC Countries
(in £ million)

	Exports	Imports	Visible Balance
1970	4,920	2,889	+2,031
1971	5,633	2,949	+2,684
1972	5,677	3,482	+2,195
1973	6,908	4,954	+1,954
1974	9,064	6,459	+2,605
1975	11,139	6,693	+4,446
1976	13,877	8,292	+5,585
1977	16,917	10,279	+6,638
1978	18,037	11,165	+6,872
1979	18,933	13,680	+5,253
1980	21,598	14,876	+6,722
1981	22,400	15,040	+7,360
1982	23,615	16,813	+6,802
Jan-Sept 1983	18,487	14,901	+3,586

Comparing the surpluses with the rest of the world with the deficits in the Common Market, we see that from the time we joined until 1982, the very large surpluses of the former made good the deficits of the latter, so that there was an overall surplus throughout those years ranging from £2,000 millions to over £6,000 millions. But the deficit with the other EEC countries has been gradually mounting up and for 1983 it exceeds the surplus gained elsewhere. As a result, we now have a substantial minus figure of £1,668 millions for a nine-month period, so that we are now truly importing more manufactured goods than we are exporting for the first time since we became an industrial nation. The figures in the Tables suggest that our position is getting steadily worse, but the deterioration is with the rest of the Common Market rather than elsewhere. No one disputed the estimate given in the House of Commons that 'They send us ten cars for every one we send them and for every £8 worth of manufactured goods we import from them, we only export £5 worth in return, and that means a loss of one million jobs.' It is true that our manufactured goods tend to be more expensive in the Common Market than those they compete against. Much less has been said about why it should be so. Among the reasons are two that are not sufficiently discussed: the effect agricultural protectionism has had cumulatively upon our other industries since 1946, and the way the Common Agricultural Policy has militated against our interests since 1973.

Before examining these reasons, it must be acknowledged that the export of our oil has played a major part in forcing up the value of the pound in the foreign exchange market to the detriment of our other exports. Our policy in extracting oil is almost the opposite to Norway's. Her view is simply that it is a precious natural resource, which once gone will never be replaced. Better to conserve the supplies by limiting its extraction and to forgo the short-term advantage of exporting it. Norway will still have oil when ours has long since gone. In contrast, the United Kingdom has chosen to become a major oil exporter, the second largest in the world. The total amount extracted from our North Seas in 1983 was 114,460,000 tonnes. Of that, 35 per cent – 40,820,000 tonnes – was exported to the rest of the Common Market. It may be wondered why we should despatch so much abroad while other oil-producing countries continue to limit their exports. The alternative, we have been told by the EEC Commissioner for energy policy, is that a common energy policy will be introduced. The others in the Common Market require the oil on favourable terms, and we are in no position to deny them what they want because, as we have learnt over the common fisheries policy, our part of the North Sea is not exclusively British, as it was before 1973. It is part of the European Community. Just as the EEC has exercised dominion over the fish that swim in the sea, so it can – and for the same reason – claim comparable rights over the oil beneath the fish.

The export of oil to the rest of the Common Market is worth £6,041 millions a year; all that money must be paid for in sterling, which has to be bought in the foreign exchange market by selling francs, deutschmarks and the other currencies of the Common Market. Each of those transactions tends to cause our currency to go up in value in the foreign exchange market and one of theirs to go down. The consequence is plain: as the pound goes up in value, all our exports to them are made more expensive, while our imports from them become cheaper. The value of our oil exports to the rest of the Common Market is

116

about the same as a million Renaults. Some estimates have been made about how far the export of our manufactured goods has been prejudiced by this, and while there must be some debate as to the extent, there can be no doubt that it is serious. Oil as an industry is highly capitalised and does not employ many people compared with our manufacturing industries, so displacing the export of manufactured goods with oil exports inevitably causes a net loss of jobs.

To limit oil extractions as Norway is doing, retaining it primarily for our own use, would make it easier for our manufacturing industries to compete on the Continent. A calculation of the approximate number of jobs lost as a result of exporting oil to the Common Market is not impossible. The Treasury has admitted that during 1979 and 1980 between one third and one half of the pound's strength on the foreign exchange market was due to the export of oil, and in that period the pound rose by 25 per cent. Today, of course, we export more than twice the amount of oil we did in 1979-1980. To bring this export of oil to an end would have the effect of devaluing the pound by at least 20 per cent. To reduce the price of our manufactured goods in the EEC by that amount would make them as competitive as they were before we began exporting oil. Our industrialists would agree unanimously that their prospects of success would then be transformed. Translated into terms of employment, it might not be unreasonable for about 500,000 jobs to be regained. The Treasury computer model available in the House of Commons confirms that a 20 per cent devaluation would ensure another 456,800 jobs within four years and in three years our current account in the balance of payments would go up by no less than £7,642 millions! As it is, our manufacturing output is very much lower than what it was on the day we joined the Common Market, and it is still declining. So long as we are bound by its terms of membership, most economists agree that to foretell a change for the better is to trade in false hopes.

Observers who compare the state of our manufacturing industries with those of the rest of the Common Market often claim that ours are less modern and less streamlined than theirs. Whichever of our industries they speak of, the same seems to be said. Since the War we have not been spending our capital on up-to-date plant and machinery; we have not pursued productivity or innovation. One reason for this has not received much attention. It has its roots in recent history. Although the CAP only came into being after the Treaty of Rome was signed in 1957, its protectionist principles were already in force in each of the member states; indeed, they had been, with varying degrees of severity, for generations. In 1940 the late Professor C.W. Guillebaud wrote an interesting study of *Hitler's New Economic Order in Europe* in which he attributed to Dr Walter Funk, the Minister of National Economy in Hitler's Germany, the idea of a system of stable agricultural prices, 'insulated from the wide fluctuations of the world market and divorced from the general level of prices at which food can be raised overseas'. He went on to say that France would benefit no less than Germany from such an agricultural policy. Dr Paul Einzig, one of the most prolific of all economic writers, spent much of his subsequent career attacking Professor Guillebaud's views and, after the War, when the Treaty of Rome was signed, showed that there was not a scintilla of difference between the principles of the CAP as set out in Article 39 of the Treaty of Rome and the New Economic Order. This distinguished European (born in Transylvania, educated in Budapest and Paris) described the Common Market as the New Economic Order without Hitler. The Treaty of Rome did little more than formalise the high level of protectionism that each of the Six had experienced for many years previously.

They were therefore accustomed to high food prices, and industrial employers within the Six had to pay higher wages in the post-war years than those in the United Kingdom to compensate for that. As a broad generalisation, one quarter of employees' incomes went on food in the Six, compared with one fifth for the British employee. His labour costs being lower, it was not necessary for the British industrialist to concern himself so much with labour productivity, so, unlike his Continental counterpart, he was not under pressure to invest a high proportion of his capital on new plant and machinery. Once we became bound by the CAP and food prices began to rise, our employees, anxious to maintain their standard of living, demanded and received considerable wage increases, necessarily greater than those of the Six over the same period.

British companies were now in a dilemma. They were compelled to pay wages comparable to those of their competitors, but while the latter had the advantage of having obtained a higher rate of labour productivity by modernising their factories in the past, ours had failed to do so because it had not been necessary for them. The sudden artificial rise in food prices therefore had the effect of pricing us out of the market.

If the EEC had been founded upon the principles of a free trade area instead of a customs union, this difficulty would never have arisen. The difference between the two is significant for us, as a people who have traded in the markets of the world. In a free trade area, each country brings down its barriers against other member states, but pursues whatever trade policy it likes with other countries outside the free trade area. A customs union requires its member states not only to bring down the internal barriers but also put up the same barriers as the rest of the customs union against every other country in the world. Membership of a free trade area would have allowed us to go on buying our food from the low-cost suppliers of the world and so continue with comparatively low wages while keeping the same standard of living. To quantify the number of jobs lost directly as a result of this sudden rise in labour costs is obviously not possible, but it must be equally obvious that it has been a major element causing us to lose a large share of our domestic market as well as making it extremely difficult to sell our manufactured goods in the rest of the Common Market. At least, every industrialist seems to blame his high labour costs for failure to export; if these costs were ten per cent less, most industrialists say their disadvantages would be overcome. Reducing the nation's food bill by £3,000 millions, as we could outside the CAP, would not go as far as that, but it might remove one third of the disadvantage.

A more serious matter is the way our own agricultural protectionism has diverted capital away from manufacturing industries to agriculture. It is a process that began the day the system of price support came into effect. In fact, a policy of price support would be pointless unless it gave resources to farming by taking them away from other industries where they would have gone naturally. The cost of the price support was calculated in the Chapter 'Where's Our Money Gone?' It came, in 1984 terms, to £62,000 millions. It is a sum of money so staggering that it is difficult to comprehend, though perhaps one way of doing it is to compare it with the capital of our largest manufacturing companies. Vickers has a capital of £100 millions; Metal Box, £193 millions; Tate & Lyle, £240 millions; Courtaulds, £357 millions; Guest, Keen & Nettlefold, £366 millions; and British Oxygen, £855 millions. The combined capital of all these great companies is £2,111 millions, yet it is a tiny proportion of the money diverted to agriculture – about one thirtieth.

This diversion of public money not into farming but into landowning has been to the prejudice of our manufacturing industries in two ways, and both are important in considering the problem of unemployment. In the first place, the means by which this money has been transferred is, of course, through taxes, and every company has had to pay over a proportion of its profits. Money lost in that way cannot be invested in new plant or modernisation. Worse still, the research and development that is a vital part of any modern enterprise tends to be the first casualty. If only ten per cent of the £62,000 millions the government has extracted from the general body of taxpayers since price support began came directly from manufacturing industries, it would still be the capital of tens of thousands of companies, and the cumulative effect over the years could be very serious.

There is a second reason why the diversion of public money to agriculture has prejudiced our manufacturing industries. Capital will always seek the highest return, either the highest rate of interest or the most favourable prospect of capital appreciation or a combination of the two. As soon as taxpayers' money is spent in any sphere of commerce, there is an immediate change in the price mechanism which automatically distorts asset values, either by increasing or reducing them from the level they would otherwise have had. If the spending of public money in the commercial sphere fails to do that, it means its effect has been neutral – and therefore futile. Now, if the consequence of the public spending is that asset values go up, there are observers on the touchline waiting to take advantage: sometimes they are called investment analysts, but they include a whole tribe of people whose business is the management of money.

For years they left agriculture alone. It was no place to put their clients' money, still less a pension fund craving for a blend of security and a reasonable return. The City generally preferred to leave farming to farmers. The Common Agricultural Policy has changed all that. The infusion of outside capital into agricultural land has been staggering.

The first to invest were the clearing banks. Though the system of price support was firmly established in 1949, the farmers only owed the banks £127 millions. Between some 500,000 farmers, it was a pretty modest amount, less than £300 a farmer. Since then it has climbed up steadily, though it was still modest until 1973, and even up until 1979 it had not reached billions of pounds. Once the significance of Peter Walker's call for maximum production was understood in the City, the banks' lending went ahead as fast as farmers could be persuaded to borrow. From £1,800 millions in February 1980 it rose to £3,300 millions three years later, and the figures were reflected in the upswing of the value of our farmland, as we saw in Chapter 3.

The Bank of England publishes *Financial Statistics* and in February 1984 it showed a still further increase in bank lending. The total for all clearing banks within the United Kingdom comes to £5,079 millions. A further £91 millions has been borrowed from foreign banks, for it is common knowledge among larger landowners that it is worthwhile to borrow from the Swiss banks, which are willing to lend at 5½ per cent. How many have done so cannot be told, though it is unlikely to be more than a thousand of them; still, that is a considerable sum for each one, and it looks as if those who have sought that money have primarily been institutional landowners. Lloyds Bank have also issued some figures to show that hire purchase companies, frequently subsidiaries of banks, have lent a further £100 millions; the merchant banks, £900 millions; private mortgagees, £300 millions; and the Agricultural Mortgage

Corporation, £500 millions. The latter is a quasi-official body that borrows in the City to relend to farmers who are owner-occupiers. Its loans to agriculture on 31 March 1947 (just before price support began) totalled £8,205,842, about £32 per farmer eligible for assistance. The present debt represents about £4,000. This twelve-fold increase in real terms is a measure of the City's willingness to lend to a branch of our economy when the asset values have become so distorted.

What would have happened, we might ask, if these billions of pounds had not been invested in agriculture? Every bank manager in the land was exhorted to advance money to agriculture; the owner of farmland had become a good risk, especially if he was able to deposit his title deeds with the bank. Compared with anything other businessmen could offer, what perfect security! Before closing on the deal, the bank manager must always contemplate the unpleasant possibility of having to foreclose on his client. To foreclose on a farm when the maximum of 75 per cent of its value has been lent could be disagreeable, but with land values rapidly moving upwards after 1979, it was not a serious risk for any bank. To lend that same money to a businessman whose security was a factory, a foundry, a warehouse, an office building or a fleet of lorries was a very different kettle of fish. At the best of times to lend 75 per cent of the value of such assets would have its perils; to lend even half as much at a time of industrial recession and rising unemployment would be positively foolhardy. Yet businessmen were, in their legions, seeking quite small advances from their banks, often offering security to cover the whole loan, and they were being refused. The more they were refused, the greater the number of company liquidations and individual bankruptcies. Any bank manager in a market town is able to confirm the prejudice he had to have against the ordinary businessman in favour of the farmer – provided he owned his own land. It was the natural and inevitable result of a policy that favoured one branch of the economy against others, and expressed that favour by giving it vast sums of public money. The bank managers were not to blame: like the farmers, they were working the system given to them by the policy makers.

The effect on employment was no less inevitable. Agriculture by 1979, and even by 1973, had long since ceased to be a major employer; it had become very capital intensive, so its expansion did not increase employment on the land – rather the reverse, as the Table in Chapter 4 shows. The thousands of businesses whose applications for a bank advance were rejected were in the aggregate the employers of probably hundreds of thousands, perhaps millions. So let us assume that bank lending to agriculture had remained at less than £2,000 millions after 1980; it would follow that a further £2,500 millions would have become available for other businesses. Many of the applications were for only £10,000 or less, so perhaps 250,000 businesses could have had the help they sought. We enter the realm of speculation in trying to gauge what number of them would have survived if they had got the loan they asked for, or how many would have expanded. What is reasonably certain is that this massive transfer of wealth has been a substantial cause of making our unemployment worse.

No less considerable has been the part played by other City institutions in diverting the nation's money to agriculture. In the 1950s they owned very little farmland, and even by 1966 the insurance companies, the main institutional investors, owned only 83,090 acres, and in the following year purchased a mere 1,981. By the time the Northfield Committee was appointed to examine the subject in 1977 it was steadily increasing and had reached 270,000 acres. Total ownership by the City institutions was then 530,000 acres. By 1982, according to an estimate by John Myers in the *New Law Journal* (29 July 1983) the City institutions owned 882,300 acres and were acquiring further land at a rate that would soon take them over the million acre mark.

Mr Anthony Steel of Reading University has carried out an intensive survey into the way the institutions have taken an interest in agriculture. By enquiring of no less than four hundred of them, he reached the conclusion that 54 pension funds owned 319,000 acres, which they valued at £414 millions; 22 insurance companies owned 449,300 acres valued at £584 millions, and 10 property unit trusts owned 114,000 acres valued at £148 millions. They were adding 67,000 acres in 1982, so that it is probable that the total would now, in 1984, be just over 1,000,000 acres, which tallies with John Myers' estimate. Their valuation must be questioned, and is probably based on the purchase price, for it comes to only £1,300 an acre, and it is common knowledge that they have preferred to buy good quality arable land rather than any other. By now the real value could be twice as much, but obviously we ought to take the lower figure in speaking of the diversion of capital. Even so, it means that in the last decade about £1,000 millions or so has been put into land by the City instead of elsewhere, and it most certainly would have gone elsewhere if we had not subscribed to the Common Agricultural Policy. Perhaps some of it would have been invested in gilt-edged securities or office development, but investment managers insist that it is unwise to place more than a certain proportion of their funds into either of them, just as most of them have been saying that it is wise to put about twelve per cent into agriculture.

Mr Robert Beckman, who is both the Editor of *Investors Bulletin* and manages funds of some £48 millions, has written an interesting book, *The Downwave*, in which he speaks of a coming depression. Referring to the massive amount of capital the City has poured into agricultural land, he says: 'Institutional investors have helped to support the market and push prices to levels which bear no relationship to the potential profitability of the businesses or the land they have been buying.'

These hundreds of millions of pounds have done nothing to create more wealth; the money has merely gone towards forcing up the value of land. Money invested in almost every other way makes work for other people: institutional purchase of land has contributed to unemployment in the countryside, because invariably the institutions have tried to amalgamate farms – the fewer tenants, the easier and cheaper to administer the estate – and they have encouraged arable farming which provides less employment, to the detriment of livestock.

Now let us come to two subordinate causes of unemployment. They are almost trivially small compared with those considered already, though not trivial to those concerned. The fall in the number of farm workers has been noted already in Chapter 4: 80,000 of them have lost their jobs since we began to go over to the system of import levies. By artificially raising the price of wheat and barley, the new system gave additional support to arable farming at the expense of the livestock producers who have always formed the sector of agriculture where the greater number of men and women were employed. The jobs lost among stockmen and herdsmen were not made good in arable farming, so that there was a net loss of employment. Sadly, many of them have been unsuccessful in seeking other work.

Then there is the closure of the sugar refineries. This followed the demise of the Commonwealth Sugar Agreement when we entered the Common Market. We now import much less cane sugar from the developing countries in the Commonwealth, and we are not allowed to import any from Australia. The number of people employed at the Tate & Lyle refineries was 6,477 in April 1977. Now it is 3,235.

I have not in these calculations referred to the fall in our exports of manufactured goods to those countries from whom the CAP prevents us buying our food. When we severed the links, our exports suffered obviously. For example, we exported 63,600 motor vehicles to Australia in 1970; ten years later the number was down to 9,440. But it is difficult to disentangle the job losses due to this from those already enumerated, and we must be careful to avoid double counting. Besides, on the evidence already cited, it is plain that, after making every allowance for the number of jobs gained in the industries supporting agriculture, not less than two million British people have lost their jobs as a result of the agricultural policy. It could well be more than that.

8/The Poorest Victims

For many years now we have been told of the millions of our fellow humans who go without food and who die prematurely simply because they have not enough to eat. No one knows quite how many they are. Estimates vary between about three hundred and about four hundred million. Whatever the number may be, any agricultural policy pursued by us that causes more people to go hungry in the world is indefensible. Yet that is exactly what is happening: our policy is playing a major part in causing millions of people to go very hungry and, as each year goes by, it affects even more.

As this is undoubtedly the gravest charge to make against our agricultural policy, and as it reflects against those responsible for pursuing it, the facts to support it must be examined very carefully. So let us try to answer the following questions:

1 Are there resources available to enable these hundreds of millions to eat enough food?

2 If the resources are available, what are the reasons for them not getting that food?

3 Have we ourselves done anything wrong? And how can we put it right?

The most obvious resource necessary for growing food is suitable land. According to the most recent *Production Year Book* of the Food and Agriculture Organisation, this planet of ours has a land surface of 33,750 million acres. 23,345 million of them are mountains, deserts or places where no vegetation can prosper except at inordinate cost. Another 5,000 million of them are of forest which, if we are sensible, we will let them so remain. Not quite all the remainder is suitable for arable cropping; but making every reasonable allowance for setting aside the poorer quality land (though it is the kind of land we have seen fit to grow wheat upon in our own country) there remains an area that is still vast. Christopher Robins, in a paper prepared for War on Want in 1975, prepared the following Table from data obtained from the Voluntary Committee on Overseas Aid and Development. I have compared the salient figures with those in the FAO *Production Year Book*, and though there have been some changes, they confirm the essential point made by Mr Robins, that the human race has all the land it needs to cultivate.

Land Availability and Use (million acres)

		Australia & NZ	North America	South America	Europe	Africa	USSR	Asia
1	Total area	2,030	5,210	4,330	1,180	7,460	5,520	6,760
2	Area available for arable crops	380	1,150	1,680	430	1,810	880	1,550
3	Area cultivated	40	590	190	380	390	560	1,280
4	Cultivated area as percentage of potential arable land	11	51	11	88	22	64	83

Data from: *Action for Development*, VCOAD, May 1975

Europe thus makes considerable use of its arable land, and by now this use probably exceeds 88 per cent. Of course, this refers to Europe in the proper sense – twenty-five countries, and not just the ten in the EEC – and it gives us quite a good bench mark to judge what is happening in the other continents. Asia's 83 per cent is due largely to the remarkable achievement of China. There, despite its hundreds of millions, visitors confirm that no one seems to go hungry. The principles of farming are an example to other countries whose natural disadvantages are trifling compared with China's. A huge area of China cannot be cultivated at all, in fact, most of it is unploughable, so to feed her massive population she has done almost the opposite of what others have been doing. The land itself is not nationalised; most of it belongs to the local communities, and each district or village owns its own land, with elected representatives managing the village estate. What does not belong to the local community is vested in individuals who are thus able to cultivate their own smallholdings. It means that every peasant (an honoured term in China) has a close and personal interest in making the land prosper. Once, millions of Chinese might die in a single year from floods devastating huge areas or from a drought that might last a whole season through. These may be now a matter of history: rivers have been dammed by the work of hundreds of thousands, fetching and carrying stones and earth, and now an even flow of water never seems to fail them. The villages do not buy in their fertilisers, nor expensive machinery; they rely on low-cost methods in every stage of their year's work. Livestock are fed on food that costs nothing except the labour of bringing it to them, and much of it is in the form of human left-overs. Cereals, such as rice and wheat, are grown for human consumption; and these are fertilised by the stock's manure, compost and anything else that can improve the soil, including human excreta. Herbicides, pesticides and fungicides appear to have no place: the hoe and the hook serve instead; they are cheap and they find work for the many hands available. Besides, by adhering to rotations, as we used to do before the agrochemical industry entered the field, they have little need for weed and pest control.

To applaud their ways is not to imply that they should be imported here, but they deserve applause because they succeed and because they suit the needs, resources and temperament of the Chinese people. That 317 million arable acres can be enough to feed 1,008 million people is, at least, an indication of what can be done. In terms of cost, it is low-input farming. It is also very efficient indeed, if efficiency is about doing a job in a competent and cost-effective manner.

A less successful brand of communism is that of the USSR, for according to the Table only 64 per cent of her arable land is cultivated. It is eloquent enough testimony to the ineptitude of central control.

Africa and South America are more important for our purposes. It is here that the worst hunger is to be found and the millions die. Only 22 per cent of Africa's arable land is cultivated, and 11 per cent of South America's. It points decisively to a dreadful waste of the most precious form of wealth that nature has given us. Worse still is the correlation between idle acres and empty bellies that exists in particular countries in each of those two continents. The Sudanese are among the hungriest of all, yet only one tenth of Sudan's arable land is cultivated. Even an approximate estimate of the percentage of untilled land in Zaire is difficult, such is the state of that country and her people. It is likely to be over 90 per cent and most of her people fail to have one proper meal in the course of the day.

South America possesses 16 per cent of the world's arable land; and it possesses also millions of people who, though they may not starve to death as in other parts of the world, suffer acutely from malnutrition. They eat the wrong kinds of food, to some extent because too much of their farming is orientated towards cash crops for export, and unfortunately an excess of bananas, coffee or sugar makes for a doubtful diet. In the case of Columbia, over half of her good farmland is lying idle. In Chile, Uruguay, Argentina and Brazil there are millions of acres that are simply no longer farmed. In Brazil it is often said that the country could feed the whole of the world if need be. It consists of 3,250,000 square miles, and if all the forests were uprooted (heaven forbid that it should happen) the land is so rich that it would yield enough cereals to give every member of the human race 6 pounds a day, yielding 9,000 calories. That is three times more than is necessary. It is one measure of what the world is capable of producing.

Several studies have been carried out by FAO and other agencies, and all of them confirm there is no shortage of land in the world to be cultivated. *The World Food Problem: a Report by the President's Science Advisory Committee*, published in 1967, showed that only about 44 per cent of the world's land potentially capable of growing arable crops was being cultivated. That proportion was bad enough then; most experts agree that it is now likely to be worse. Perhaps the most startling conclusion was reached by Professor Roger Revelle. Writing about 'Food and population' for *Scientific American* in 1974 he argued that the world could sustain a population of between 40 and 50 billions. That is ten times more than it is at present.

Let us admit that the world's population is increasing; but let us also ask ourselves why it should be so. Susan George and others have done much to establish the link between poverty and large families. A succession of children (preferably sons) will provide security in sickness and old age in a society where state benefits and social security are unknown. The poorer you are in a poor country, the more children you want to bring into the world. In the other direction, one cannot establish any necessary connection between a high density of population and hunger, as numerous countries such as Belgium, Netherlands and ourselves can show. Zaire is the opposite extreme.

Looking again at the FAO *Production Year Book*, it is clear we have 3,500 million acres of the world being cultivated; and that represents a little less than one acre per head of the population. Without much difficulty and without doing any ecological damage, we could make it an acre and a half. In the United Kingdom there are some 21 million arable acres, yielding half the food eaten by 55 million people. True, the comparison is not altogether fair as it excludes our pasture used for sheep and cattle; on the other hand, we can afford to be very extravagant in how we produce our food, most of our cereals, for example, going to feed our livestock. An acre and a half should be enough for the grossest feeder wherever he may live in the world.

It may be argued that some of the poorer countries are in need of land reform, for in parts of South America especially there are international companies holding onto vast areas that they fail to cultivate. But where land reform has been carried out it has seldom been a solution in itself; besides, the amount of land that could be released in that way can come to only a small fraction of what is now uncultivated.

So to speak of any shortage of the most important resource of all for the production of food is to take us far into the realm of the fanciful. Labour and capital are the other factors of production. Labour is manifestly there: people by the millions, and the millions can grow the food for further millions. As to capital, very little is needed, as it would be foolish indeed to introduce capital to displace labour, as our own farmers have found it profitable to do. The simplest ploughs, the most elementary reaping methods and all other kinds of low or intermediate technology are what are needed. To send our 78 horsepower tractors and massive combines (the sort of thing some people have suggested in the past) would be self-defeating. Seed suitable for the soil, climate and terrain are less easy to supply, but the Taiwanese are in a position to help many countries, even those dissimilar to their own, and so also are several others in the Third World which have overcome their own difficulties. Lack of irrigation is a problem in most developing countries, and here capital is required. It is generally agreed that there is no shortage of water, even in places like Sahel, but extracting it, either by making wells or diverting it from rivers, will require money. Outside funds may be necessary in most of the countries, but comparatively speaking, it would be a small sum.

Two other resources must not be overlooked: fertilisers and pesticides. Western Europe consumes about twenty-one times as much fertiliser as the whole of Africa, yet its area of cultivation is less, as the Table shows. Western European farmers can afford to buy it; Africans cannot. The price has risen considerably in the last decade, from less than £20 a ton in 1971 to about £170 today, and while it is true that one of the reasons for this increase of 850 per cent has been the rise in oil prices, not a ton of this fertiliser would have been sold in Western Europe unless the purchasers had been able to afford the price. Now the reason they can afford the price of fertiliser is very simple: the more it goes up, the more their farmgate prices also go up. The price the farmer in the EEC receives for his wheat, milk or nearly every other kind of food he produces is fixed for him by the EEC, and the EEC in fixing the price takes into account his costs. In a word, the higher price of the fertiliser is passed on automatically to the customer who buys the food.

The Third World cannot do business like that. Their customers, most of them too poor to buy enough food anyway, are in no position to pay higher prices every time farmers want them. The fertilisers, of course, are manufactured in the main by a few great international companies; they are controlled in the West, and their first market is Western agriculture because it is for them a certain and profitable outlet.

Our high-input/high-output system requires us to use ever more fertilisers, but as with most other inputs, the law of diminishing returns applies. In the United Kingdom the average amount of fertiliser applied to an acre in 1961/62 was 31 units. By 1981/82, the average had increased to 93 units. This three-fold increase in fertilisers has failed to increase yields proportionately. The figures available for fertiliser use apply to all agricultural land and no separate estimate is obtainable for individual crops; but I think most arable farmers would agree that the increase in the use of fertiliser on their wheat has been at least as great as the national average, and I suspect they would cede it has been substantially more. The average wheat yield in 1961/62 was 1·40 tons an acre; in 1981/82 it was 2·55 tons. This means that the increase in the use of fertiliser is in the ratio 3 to 1, while the increase in yields is only 1·82 to 1. The downward trend is pellucidly plain, and every agricultural scientist sees it continuing. He also recognises that much of the increase in wheat yields is due to better varieties of seed; were it not for those improvements, the ratio would show an even worse downward trend.

The Fertiliser Manufacturers' Association publishes each year a report and it shows how much their industry has expanded since we pursued a high-cost farming policy. The following comes from their annual reports.

UK Consumption of Inorganic Fertilisers

Year	Consumption (tonnes)	Percentage increase on previous year
1977/78	1,980,000	3·6
1978/79	2,021,000	2·1
1979/80	2,115,000	6·6
1980/81	2,229,000	3·4
1981/82	2,356,000	5·7

How different it is in the Third World! There the use of fertiliser is diminishing. Instead of being able to use more fertilisers to grow more food, higher prices force them to use less and thus to grow less food. Yet one ton of fertiliser applied on their land, if previously unfertilised, could yield an extra ten tons of grain. A ton of fertiliser in the Third World is likely to produce about five times more food than the same ton applied on land in our own country.

In the language of the economist, that is a gross misallocation of resources. If there was a genuine free market, the resource would go where it would yield the greatest returns. That does not happen because a price support policy for our farmers – and for farmers in other developed countries – makes it impossible for resources to be allocated in the most sensible manner. When certain politicians and farming leaders in Britain call for still higher output, they are in a position to have the farmgate prices increased to make good the higher costs of the inputs. Neither individual farmers nor governments in the poor countries can compete with that.

That is not the end of the matter. These artificial fertilisers are exhaustible. Great reserves may still exist, but they get less all the time, and as we in Britain and, to some extent, in other developed countries use them at a speed that is accelerating, it follows that reserves are being lost at a quickening pace.

Not long ago, I went to see a great area, several square miles in size, in West Africa where they were extracting phosphate. Enormous trucks were taking several tons at a time to the docks about eighty miles away, and there it was despatched to farmers who could afford to buy it, ours included. In that same country there were tens of thousands who were fortunate if they got a single meal in a day; families were suffering from the diseases of malnutrition, and they were dying.

Experts repeatedly sound the alarm about the way we are using up these fertilisers. Again and again, they repeat that there will not be enough in the 1990s. Perhaps one quotation will be enough; it is from *By Bread Alone*, by Lester R. Brown and Erik P. Eckholm:

Farmers in much of the world are confronted not only with higher fertiliser cost as the cost of energy rises, but also with lessening returns on fertiliser use. The amount of grain produced with each additional ton of fertiliser used is beginning to diminish at the global level, largely because of the high levels of use in such areas as North America, Western Europe and Japan. Each additional million tons of fertiliser applied by the world's farmers now adds less food than was added by the preceding million tons. The total level of chemical fertilisers required at the century's end may be more than four times the 800 million tons being used today.

No country in the world is more to blame than ours. Even the rest of the EEC does not use up fertilisers on quite the scale we do (the Dutch are as extravagant as we are per farmer but the total quantity they use is very much less). The United States, Canada, Australia and other major grain growing countries have plenty of land to spare and their land is much cheaper, so they are not under the same pressure to maximise yields.

As to pesticides, their importance to the Third World is greater than it is to us. Ecologists can present a very persuasive case against their use, and in an ideal world, it might be possible for the African and the South American to farm as the Chinese do. But a century or more of colonial influence has had its effect, and a great part of both those continents is now dependent upon monoculture. If land can be made to grow coffee or tea or cocoa or sugar or bananas or copra or anything else more economically than some other land, then it has been. In one sense, it is eminently sensible that agriculture should be arranged like that; but it would be unfair to infer that this is the result of a free market system. The latter implies free trade and the removal of all barriers that separate a willing buyer from a willing seller. Such a robust principle did not fit in with the paternalistic thinking of the colonial rulers. France, Belgium, the Netherlands, Spain and Portugal, besides ourselves, all had bilateral arrangements with their colonial possessions that militated against the most elementary principles of free trade. A Frenchman trying to buy sugar in Barbados or an Englishman trying to buy maize in Mozambique would soon have been sent packing. Barbadian sugar was planted, grown and harvested for Britain or some other part of the Empire, and no one else. All the old imperial powers behaved in the same way. In return, each of the empires took their colonial chicks under their wings and protected them from the ravages of a rival power. Cash cropping has been the consequence. A great part of an erstwhile colony, once made over to a single kind of crop, cannot easily now diversify into other forms of agriculture. Pundits from Brussels or London descend, from time to time, on these countries and tell them they should plant this or that instead, but the pundits usually arrive in total ignorance of how each kind of monoculture has developed subsidiary industries. Mills, factories, processing plants, research stations and a whole transport network, including perhaps a railway company to take the cash crop to the mills and then on to the docks; all these have grown up in most of the former colonies to handle the coffee, sugar or other cash crop, and they may employ more people than the plantations themselves. Since all these monocultures are prone to diseases, pests and other things that can decimate a crop, they cannot continue without pesticides.

The other special feature of the Third World is that most of it is tropical; and the insects, mites, ticks, nematodes, fungi, bacteria, weeds, rodents, molluscs, crustacea and viruses that can blight the life of a farmer tend to be more virulent, persistent and otherwise troublesome than those we encounter in our kinder and temperate climate. It has been said that food lost on the stalk through pests and disease in poor countries can be one third of what is harvested, and of what is harvested forty per cent can be lost in storage.

But the price of all pesticides has rocketed upwards, and even in real terms they are now many times more expensive than they were ten years ago. As with fertilisers, the cost of pesticides is taken into account when the farmer in the Common Market has his prices fixed for him. The agrochemical industry can charge accordingly. Also, as with fertilisers, our high-input/high-output ratio requires an increasing use of pesticides. This higher demand has the inevitable result of causing prices to go up still further, to the detriment of others in the world. It follows that we are not altogether paying the true cost of our high-input/high-output system. We are passing some part of it on to the poorest people in the world.

So let us now answer that first question in a sentence. All the resources are there on our planet to enable everyone to eat the food they should have, but so long as we pursue a high-output policy, financed by a price support system, there is little chance of fertilisers being used to the best advantage; and fertilisers and pesticides will be made artificially more expensive and beyond the means of those who need them most. And in that respect the policy makers of Britain are as responsible as anyone else in the world. These men have been influenced by our agrochemical industry and they have listened to its special pleading too much. Why were our policy makers induced to give our farmers a subsidy of taxpayers' money to buy phosphate fertilisers in

1951? Why was that subsidy extended to other fertilisers later? When a definitive history of British agriculture for the post-war years is written, perhaps its author will lay bare the truth.

Now let us turn to the second question, namely, if the resources are available, what are the reasons why these hundreds of millions are not getting the food they should have? Granted that fertilisers and pesticides are important and we are being selfish in their use, that still does not explain why those millions of acres of good arable land are not cultivated. The answer is really a matter of common sense, once one thinks a little about it. The business of growing food can be long and laborious, and from the time one begins the process to the time one gets paid for all the work, a year is likely to go by. There are millions of farmers in the world, from multi-millionaires to peasants in abject poverty, but they have one thing at least in common. None of them are minded to begin growing food for other people unless they are reasonably sure that they are going to get paid for it.

All those hundreds of millions cannot, in fact, pay for the food they want. Their need for food is one thing; their capacity to exchange some money for it is another. If there are about four hundred million of us dying of undernutrition or malnutrition, then it is about the same number who simply are too poor to buy the food they need. The prime and fundamental cause of this mass hunger is poverty.

How then can this poverty be overcome? Doling out money from the exchequers of the wealthier nations is a plausible possibility, but obviously it would do nothing to put matters right permanently. Sending them our surplus food is an alternative canvassed by the leaders of the NFU and our chemical industry, but this has several objections. Much of our surplus food is of a kind that would be totally unsuitable, nor could its future supply be assured; but above all it would be ludicrous for us, as high-cost producers, to send food to people who cannot afford to pay for it, when the same type of food could be exported to them by low-cost producers in Australia, the United States and elsewhere. If the richer nations of the world are going to organise a scheme of food aid, it ought to be from those low-cost producers, rather than ourselves.

Another remedy is what the Third World has repeatedly sought in words that have become a cliché – trade not aid. Unfortunately, the meaning of that repeated request fails to be understood. Having had the good fortune of visiting fifteen of the countries concerned, including two of the poorest of them, I have had spelt out for me in plain terms what they would like: it is that we should allow them to sell to us what they can produce. Now what they can sell is the produce of their soil. There is little else they can offer us or anyone else, except for the lucky ones who have mineral deposits. The EEC, through the Lomé Convention, may say they can export their manufactured goods into the Common Market, as if hundreds of thousands were making cars or washing machines or computers. So long as they remain developing countries, any secondary or manufacturing industry will be primitive or non-existent. Of course, there are some factories in some parts of the Third World, but generally they are small and there to supply a local need, and quite incapable of embarking upon any serious export trade. Others have textile mills, but the EEC has imposed severe restrictions upon textiles being exported to us. Quotas have been introduced by the Multi-Fibre Arrangement, so that fewer textiles are allowed in from the countries affected than previously. It has meant that their workers must now either produce more for a lower wage to allow other markets to be found, or produce less, and thus accept a still lower standard of life.

But the countries where there is mass hunger tend to be those where there is no other kind of work except farming. If they were able to export food, there would then be jobs available for them to grow food and so earn money; and with the money they earned they could pay for their own food. Until that opportunity comes, it seems they can never get off the launching pad, let alone launch themselves to a height where abject squalor is left behind. Getting rid of food in order to eat may appear, at first sight, too much of a paradox. So let us look at it through their eyes; and let us take one of the countries I visited. There is a part of Senegal, in West Africa, that is a microcosm of the Third World. It is along the banks of the River Senegal that divides Mauritania (perhaps the poorest of all the poor countries) from Senegal itself. This great river has, over the centuries, brought down from the hinterland rich alluvial silt, so today there are hundreds of thousands of acres of superb land; in the United Kingdom we would classify it as Grade I and value it at over £3,000 an acre. It goes uncultivated, apart from some ten thousand acres where a plantation has been established to grow sugar and tomatoes which are sent to Dacca, the capital, for local consumption, though they hope to secure an export outlet. The land is much richer than what lies beside the Nile where a million acres may afford three crops a year, where the sun shines every day and the waters of the Nile irrigate by night. Senegal could do as well as Egypt. Its river may be smaller, but it brings down more than enough water for the needs of that soil, and as in Egypt, the sun shines unfailingly. Yet not only is the land uncultivated, but there are many thousands suffering from acute hunger on that very land. I saw small children with their bellies distended and their legs emaciated, and beside them were mothers who looked as if they were in their fifties, but who would have been thirty years younger.

If anyone set about the task of cultivating that land and actually growing food, what would happen to it? He would eat his share; and he could try to sell the rest, but he would look in vain for anyone who could pay for it. All around he would see people without enough money, perhaps with no money at all, and none of them would give him a livelihood for the work he had done.

The area I visited would probably be very suitable for growing maize. It is just the crop that should be grown in the tropics and it is almost as good a basis for a poor man's meal as can be devised. Perhaps rice could also be grown there. But neither can be imported into the United Kingdom unless an import levy is paid. Under the EEC Regulations the levy on maize imported from outside the Common Market was £37.70 per tonne when this was written. The Lomé Convention gives a privilege to about fifty former colonies of the European powers known as the ACP Group (Africa, Caribbean and Pacific) by which their maize may enter on payment of a reduced levy. Today on the same date this stood at £36.60 per tonne, so on maize from Senegal there was paid £1.10 a tonne less than on maize from the United States.

Supporters of the EEC trumpet rather loudly about the Lomé Convention and frequently claim that it enables these former colonies to have free access to our market. The following Table was in *Hansard* on 1 November 1983, in answer to my Written Question.

Description	ACP Levy £/tonne	Other Third World Countries £/tonne
Paddy rice round grain	48.0447	100.5500
Paddy rice long grain	42.8975	90.2494
Husked rice round grain	60.6158	125.6859
Husked rice long grain	54.1756	112.8117
Semi-milled round grain	91.7589	198.2789
Semi-milled long grain	113.8696	242.4509
Wholly milled rice round grain	97.9455	211.1717
Wholly milled rice long grain	122.3143	259.9093
Broken rice	14.4580	32.6279

Rice, like maize, can be grown in many countries in the Third World; and obviously the more it is milled or processed there the more work is found for those who live there. A nil rate of levy would be a considerable benefit to them, but the Table shows that the more the rice is processed the higher the rate of levy. In fact, the levy is more than doubled. Third World countries outside the ACP group – and several of them are the poorest of all – pay the full levy; and if they choose to wholly mill their rice in competition with the Italians, the levy is fixed at over £200 a tonne. The levy apart, the prospect of being able to export not only maize and rice but many other kinds of food either to the United Kingdom or to any other part of the Common Market dims as the years go by and our quest for self-sufficiency shrinks the market for any exporter.

As we know, our degree of self-sufficiency exceeds a hundred per cent in numerous commodities. Beef, wheat, barley, butter, cheese, rice, malt, wheat flour, whole milk powder, skimmed milk powder, condensed milk, pigmeat, poultry meat, sugar and wine are all in surplus. Export subsidies have to be paid out to secure a place in the world market for this food and drink we do not want, and these export subsidies fill the Third World with dismay, as they do the United States, Canada, Australia, New Zealand and other countries that depend upon food exports for their trade abroad. For them to compete against us in a food war in which both sides try to undercut the other by lowering their export prices to below the cost of production is out of the question. The result is that their share of food exports to the world market is declining. The following figures tell the story. They set out the percentage of the world trade in food achieved by the Third World, and they show how much the Third World has been losing.

Year	Percentage
1960	37·1
1970	31·8
1975	28·9
1981	27·7

The figures, which are from the UN *Monthly Bulletin of Statistics*, show a remorselessly downward trend. A fall of some ten per cent of the share of trade, when it is one's principal and perhaps only source of foreign exchange, verges upon the catastrophic.

Now for the third question: What have we done wrong and how can we put it right? This can easily be answered: we should unilaterally declare a free trade policy. Two results would follow immediately for the Third World. First, they would regain the chance to supply our consumers with food (while our consumers regained their freedom to buy that food). Secondly, we would no longer be a party to the EEC's policy of dumping surplus food on the world market in competition with others who cannot afford to use their taxpayers' money in that way. As we are one of the two chief paymasters of the Common Agricultural Policy such a decision would effectively bring to an end the guarantee section of its fund that pays for that dumping.

The decision would hurt a few people, but the financial loss to some individuals and a few companies would have to be set against gains that could not be counted in money. True, opening up our own market to the outside world would go only a fraction of the distance to provide hundreds of millions with an income, but even a few million people given what they should have – and what they will never get if attitudes do not change – would be a giant step forward for them and an example for others to follow.

Having shaped the economies of some twenty or thirty countries so that they grew cash crops to our advantage, it may be said that we still owe an obligation to them to buy those crops at fair and reasonable prices. That is one argument for commodity agreements. Such long-term agreements can also be justified on purely commercial grounds, as in the case of the old Commonwealth Sugar Agreement which had to be brought to an end when we entered the Common Market. Sugar, indeed, highlights the plight of the poorest victims.

Of all the poorest victims, the cane sugar growers deserve a special mention. We in the UK have played a unique part in their declining fortunes, and it was because of our special obligation to the cane sugar growers that, when entering the EEC, we negotiated an agreement to permit their sugar to continue to come into the UK, despite the rules of the CAP which would otherwise have excluded it.

So what is this special obligation? The main countries concerned, Jamaica, Barbados, Guyana, Trinidad, Fiji, Mauritius and some others to a lesser degree, were peopled by our forefathers; and while the last of the slaves came many generations ago, it was in 1917, in the lifetime of people living today, that indentured Indians were still being taken to Guyana, Mauritius and Fiji. The system was not so very different from slavery. The Indians were coaxed by dubious promises to sign an indenture and, once transported to their destination, they were kept in bond yards for the hours when they were not marshalled into the sugar factories or out onto the cane fields. Put bluntly, they were imprisoned to stop them escaping.

For this we received the cheapest sugar in the world. It is not a portion of history that we should forget, because even to this day the British people are able to benefit from having had that cheap food, for it has made us richer than we would otherwise have been. Cheap sugar enabled us to spend more money on other items and so raise our standard of living and develop other industries. The wealth thus gained has still not yet been lost; and all of us, to a larger or lesser degree, are to this day better off as a result of hundreds of thousands of men and women gathering in a harvest of sugar cane for generations of British people to eat. It would be hard to deny that we have a moral obligation to protect their descendants from the vicisitudes of a volatile world market for sugar, made even more so by ourselves.

Thus this special obligation became a feature of our negotiations in joining the Common Market. The outcome was an agreement whereby the Commonwealth sugar producers, Australia excepted, would be allowed to export to us 1·2 million tonnes a year at prices comparable to those of Common Market growers. They were joined by Surinam, Zaire and Malagasy to form the ACP group, though the additional three countries sell only about 30,000 tons under the agreement. 1·2 million tonnes represents about half their production, so the other half has to be sold in the world market at world prices. At the time it seemed to the Commonwealth a reasonable arrangement, and only the Jamaican Minister of Agriculture, Mr John Gyles, had the foresight to see the danger ahead – that the European beet growers, armed with modern technology, would have ever increasing yields and ever larger surpluses of sugar to get rid of.

The root of the trouble is that sugar, whether cane or beet, is quite an easy crop to grow, and it can be grown in extremely difficult conditions when nothing else seems to provide a reliable crop. The forebears of today's sugar producers were shipped to these places, and there is little else they can do to earn a livelihood in them, except grow sugar. Barbados may not be typical, but its experience is worth recording. It is a coral island and the soil can be cultivated to a depth of a little more than a foot. They have been told to diversify into other forms of agriculture, and no less than fifty-five other crops have been tried. They have all failed, with the partial exception of tomatoes and a few other vegetables, which have been only a moderate success. One of my visits to Barbados coincided with the hurricane Allen when two merchant ships were swept onto the beaches and trees and houses were uprooted, to be hurled extraordinary distances. Yet the sugar cane survived. Though combed down by the tempestuous wind, it recovered its normal stance to yield only a quarter less than would have been usual.

On the other hand, the banana trees and most of the tomatoes and other crops were laid waste. Perhaps we should confess that places like Barbados ought never to have been peopled by us for the purpose of growing food; but we cannot turn the clock back now, and those who live in Barbados must take the consequences. They have gone so far in developing a tourist trade, but though the dollars and pounds may flow in, it is a trade which brings with it many drawbacks when taken beyond a certain stage, as Jamaica and the Bahamas have learnt. Some engineering and other industries have been set up, but they are on too small a scale to make exporting worthwhile or to employ as many men and women as the sugar industry.

The problems of Fiji and Mauritius are similar to those of Barbados. Trinidad has found oil, but Jamaica and Guyana, though they have bauxite to extract, are also dependent upon sugar for their people to have a livelihood worth the name. As it is, Jamaica's unemployment rate is one of the worst in the world, about thirty per cent, and its acute poverty (with no unemployment benefit or social security) has brought her unhealthily close to a Cuban brand of communism. To prevent even more people losing their jobs, the Jamaican Parliament, some years ago, made it illegal for the sugar farmers to mechanise. The decision placed them in a dilemma: mechanisation would have lowered costs and allowed them to compete on the world market that much more easily, and so part of their export trade was lost. The other cane growing countries have also put curbs upon mechanisation of varying kinds, with the same object of preventing an increase in unemployment. In any case they can hardly afford the cost of mechanisation. The Jamaican High Commission tells me that in 1972 a Jamaican could buy a new seventy-eight horse-power tractor for the price of 21 tons of sugar, but now he has to grow 50 tons to buy the same kind of tractor. Neither diversification nor mechanisation is a real solution to the problem.

Guyana, Fiji and Swaziland are the three countries that, with Queensland, can produce sugar more cheaply than anywhere else. One might suppose, therefore, that they would have first place in the world market. They don't. Like the other low-cost producers they have gone through a crisis, through being forced

143

to compete with the world's highest-cost producers, those in the EEC, whose sugar is dumped onto the world market with the aid of enormous subsidies.

Because sugar is, compared with most other crops, easy to grow, too much of it is being produced at a time when total consumption is standing still and in some countries, including our own, declining. Throughout the EEC, consumption is about 9 million tonnes a year, but production is 13 million tonnes. To this surplus must be added the 1·2 million tonnes of Commonwealth sugar. Most of the total surplus has had to be sold onto the world market; but 80 per cent of the sugar traded is sold in accordance with long term contracts at agreed prices, which means that a residual world market requires about only 5 million tonnes of sugar. Suddenly adding another 5 million tonnes obviously has a catastrophic effect upon prices. At one point in 1982 the world price went down to £83 a tonne, and for weeks on end remained at less than £100. No farmer, no matter how personally efficient or how favourably blessed with soil or climate, can grow sugar at that price. The lowest of the low-cost producers in the world need a price of £140 a tonne to break even.

Guyana is in the league of low-cost producers. Her rich land on the south Atlantic coast has been for generations a superb area for sugar; and when the world price fell to below £100 a tonne, I had the opportunity of seeing at first hand the effect it was having upon a country whose main source of foreign exchange was its sugar exports. Unless Guyana can sell sugar, the country comes to a standstill – literally. There is no oil, no petrol, no spare parts for cars or tractors, and obviously no new ones. It is difficult to imagine what happens to a country, when to carry on at all, it is forced to sell its exports at nearly half the cost of production. The consequences also happen very quickly. My wife and I stayed at the foremost hotel in the capital, owned by Trust Houses Forte, whose manager only six weeks previously had been the assistant manager of a famous hotel in London. High standards would normally prevail, and the menu for breakfast would be pretty good. In fact, we had black coffee – the poor manager could get nothing else. No bread to make toast, no flour in the capital, except in the black market. It didn't matter really to us – probably it was rather good for us – but out on the plantations it was a different story. To maintain yields, considerable quantities of fertiliser are required, so the government gave priority to them being imported; but it could not also give priority to new tractors and other machinery, nor spare parts. So on one plantation we visited four tractors were in use instead of fourteen, and the men who should have been working hard were standing about in idleness. The costs of the following year's crop would go up, the land might not be so well tilled and the harvest would suffer.

Perhaps the most vivid impression of all came when we visited a modern hospital, serving a district where many thousands lived. There were only four patients in the men's ward, and one in the women's. Yet there were hundreds of men and women waiting for operations or some other treatment in that hospital. The surgeons were there, so were the nurses, the pharmacists and all the other staff; the operating theatres were open and waiting. Everything was available except just one element – drugs. These had to be imported from abroad, principally from the UK, and there was no foreign exchange available. Whether people died as a result, I do not know for certain; one of the surgeons was convinced that they would.

An attempt has been made by the Common Market to stem the rising tide of sugar surpluses flooding over the world market, and the new regime had been introduced before our visit to Guyana. The theory of it is that EEC producers will pay for the cost of this dumping. True, it has caused a reduction from the amount of sugar produced in previous years, but there will still be a surplus of about 5 million tonnes. The EEC Commission recognises that the price given to the sugar grower in the Common Market is set so high that he can afford to pay a levy for the surplus to be dumped abroad. Worse still, the new policy assumes that a quantity of sugar equivalent to whatever may be imported from the ACP countries will be re-exported and the subsidy for its sale in the world market will be paid for by the EEC itself. This policy provides the funds needed to dump between 3 and 4 million tonnes of sugar. It nullifies the good that the agreement to import the 1·2 million tonnes may give the poorest victims among the sugar growers. It means that the sugar they grow and sell to us is used to undercut the price of the rest of their sugar.

In round figures, the Commonwealth countries have 2·5 million tonnes to export. They receive a reasonable price for half of it from the UK importers; so far, so good. But that remaining half still must be sold and at a price that is, to all intents and purposes, fixed by the quantity of surplus sugar that the EEC chooses to sell. When it resells the Commonwealth producers' sugar, plus its own surplus, the effect is still to undermine the chance of cane sugar growers being able to sell at a price over the cost of production. The longer the EEC behaves in this way, the poorer the people in Guyana, Fiji, Barbados, Jamaica and the others will become. If, in consequence, they think less of us and our ability to convince the rest of the EEC of the injustice of their sugar policy and to act accordingly, we cannot be surprised. I have visited all the cane sugar countries in recent years; they have a deep attachment to our country and its values and way of life. All of them have resisted the blandishments of Soviet Russia and Cuba. Let us not make it too difficult for them to go on doing so.

Bringing Farming
Down to Earth

9/Forward in a Lower Gear

Thus there are five groups of victims with a common interest in changing our agricultural policy: efficient British farmers, our allies overseas, ourselves as consumers, the unemployed, and the food-producers of the Third World. Changes are going to come: the damage done so far makes that certain, and many different and conflicting ideas will be advanced about what they should be. Several steps to put matters right can be inferred from the previous pages, and in this chapter they will be set out explicitly. But first of all, even if we know what action is needed, are we in a position to take it?

There are those who claim that, being bound by the Common Agricultural Policy, we have lost the right to take an independent line. Among them is my colleague, Robert Jackson, in his booklet *From Boom to Bust?* They are too pessimistic. The reality is that we have the power to change the system, provided only we have the will to do so.

In the first place, we are one of the two chief paymasters of the CAP. It collapses unless we give our money for it. Secondly, we provide the rest of the EEC with a market for their manufactured goods far in excess of what we export to them. The advantage to their manufacturing industries over ours is worth no less than £7,000 millions. The bringing down of tariff barriers between the rest of the EEC and ourselves has been very much to their advantage rather than ours. Before we joined, we imposed a higher tariff against manufactured goods imported from the Six than they placed upon our manufactured goods to them. This is not to suggest that we should revert to tariffs again: it does mean that we have absolutely nothing to fear from the threat of retaliatory action if we were to say we did not wish to be bound by the Common Agricultural Policy any longer. A tit-for-tat war over non-food items, erecting barriers and obstacles other than tariffs, would do the rest of the EEC much more damage than it could to us. Numerous economists have gone so far as to point out that such barriers would be positively beneficial for our manufacturing industries and some indeed think they are necessary if we are to reduce unemployment.

Thirdly, there is the matter of oil. We export 35 per cent of our oil to the rest of the EEC on terms favourable to them. It has assured them of much security in an insecure market. Their dependence upon our oil is a major consideration. It is a trump card.

The fourth reason is of enormous importance to our own farmers. There are parts of Western Europe – the Paris basin and most of the Netherlands are two of them – where the structure, technology and technical efficiency of the farmers are a match for our own. But speaking generally, though they are catching up, they are still behind us. The majority of them succeed in making a livelihood with low-cost methods. To dismiss them as inefficient, as so many commentators have done, is to miss the point. They are running their farms at a lower gear and surviving, and it is doubtful whether our farmers could, in the main, come down to the same gear and also survive. This is not a criticism of our farmers' skills – on the contrary, they are on the whole of the highest standard – but, as we saw, their incomes have depended upon higher levels of output year after year, so they have been forced to adapt to a system that would put them out of business if they were to reduce their output. A Common Agricultural Policy refashioned to secure lower output with lower inputs would have a penal effect upon our farmers, but leave a vast majority of those in the rest of the Common Market unscathed. It is the reason why it is in the interests of British agriculture for agricultural policy to be repatriated. So long as the mechanisms of the Common Agricultural Policy are being designed to increase the output of farm production, the policy is attractive for many of our farmers, and that is undoubtedly why most of them are in favour of it. But the minute the mechanisms are changed so as to place a limit upon output, their interests change too. We can only speculate about the rate of inflation in the future, but we can be sure of two things: there will be some rate of inflation, and any rate of inflation will have the effect of raising farm costs. How can those higher costs be paid unless farm incomes also go up? For them to be raised, farmers must either receive higher farmgate prices for the existing level of output or increase production.

An agricultural policy formulated here at home, with the interests of only British farmers, taxpayers and consumers in mind, can overcome that difficulty. But the interests of our farmers are in conflict with those of Germany, Italy, France and indeed all the rest. A large arable farmer, sitting in his study somewhere in East Anglia and surrounded by several hundred rich acres, can reflect how he prospers in a Common Market with common prices fixed throughout ten countries at a level to let peasants earn a livelihood when they are scratching about on a few hectares. Their survival-money multiplies for him into at least the price of a new Mercedes annually. His view is right, but only because it is founded upon the assumption that he is able to expand his output. Whatever device or mechanism is employed to limit production, it will place him at a disadvantage compared to the peasant farmers on the Continent. Millions of them – about twenty million in all – survived continuously for hundreds of years in Western Europe, more than twice the number today, because they could adapt to low-cost methods with the least difficulty. They were born to that way of life, lived all their lives that way, and generations of them became conditioned to surviving on the land because the technique of survival was handed down from father to son. The arable farmers of East Anglia are not made that way, and now they are the more vulnerable because of it.

We speak glibly about mountains of food surpluses. They are molehills compared with what is coming. The potential for increasing the quantity of milk and cereals throughout the Common Market is enormous. Milk yields could increase by fifty per cent on the Continent, just as they have in the United Kingdom, once their dairy breeding and technology catch up with ours. Agricultural scientists in the area of cereals have no doubt that cereal production could double in the 1990s.

So at some stage the architects of the Common Agricultural

Policy must decide how to curb these excesses. Essentially, there are two alternatives: lower prices for the farmer or quotas of production. The first would be less prejudicial to our cereal growers on good quality land; for others (cereal growers with Grade III land or worse, and dairy farmers) quotas might be less disadvantageous. Quotas would also be more suitable for the great majority of Continental farmers. Moreover, it would settle the question whether there are social reasons for a common policy. If one of the purposes of the Common Agricultural Policy is to keep people on the land, it is plain that a system of quotas will achieve that more readily than the price mechanism. This demonstrates the clash of interests between an efficient arable farmer on Grade I or Grade II land and his less efficient counterpart on the Continent. It is a major reason why a common policy must in the 1990s militate against his interests.

The argument goes to the heart of the matter. Economists argue that food should be grown in places and countries where it can be produced at the lowest cost. This is a fair policy for farmers in those countries, and it is fair for everyone who eats the food, and who can then buy it at the lowest price. The ecologist's argument is even more important, for the cost he is concerned with is a matter of life and death: everything we do on the farm is about the life or death of a plant or animal. To grow food in the places of lowest cost means in places where the input/output ratio is the most financially rewarding. Higher inputs, measured in terms of money, are most likely to mean also higher inputs ecologically (for example, more nitrates or pesticides). The connection between the two kinds of cost is obviously not exact, but a link is there none the less, and it follows that the growing of food in economically low-cost countries is likely to be at a lower ecological cost too. Ecologists are naturally (in both senses of the word) free traders.

The present CAP is the root cause of the damage done to our landscape. By goading farmers into growing arable crops where they should not be grown and penalising the keeping of livestock, it has had the effect of boosting the incomes of the larger farmer while diminishing those of the smaller ones. It has caused tens of thousands of farms to be amalgamated, and all the changes in the rural landscape that follow inevitably from forcing our farmers to do what they cannot do economically. 'Prairieisation' is an ugly word to describe an ugly process. It is what has happened over a great part of our country. Only the worst kind of farmer has gained, those who have bought land to exploit it for mercenary motives, the aggro-businessmen. Public money – the money of taxpayers and consumers, which includes the poorest among us – is subsidising these aggro-businessmen and not, in most cases, the bona fide farmer.

One farmer in Kent has been given £100,000 not to drain marshland and so change it from good pasture to being capable of growing wheat. Another farmer in Dorset is to receive a subsidy of £20,400 a year for sixty-five years for not uprooting woodland to enable wheat and other cereals to be produced. In Norfolk to avoid 748 acres of the Halvergate Marshes being drained for even more cereals to be grown, the four farmers concerned expect to receive £100,000 of public money every year for twenty years. It has been reported that £40 millions from the taxpayers will be needed to meet the claims being made under the Wildlife & Countryside Act, 1981, by farmers and landowners who would otherwise convert marshland, woodlands and sites of special scientific interests to land fit for cereals.

The Nature Conservancy Council, the Countryside Commission or indeed anyone at all has a hopeless task in trying to protect our countryside against the ravages of the assault. The money available, even if it reaches the £40 millions, will not be enough. Yet not a penny of it would be needed if it were not for the system of import levies. So long as they sufficiently raise the price of wheat, barley, maize and other arable crops to a level that makes it financially worthwhile to grow them on land that is not suitable for them and where they would otherwise be grown at a loss, farmers and landowners will continue to have an astonishing bargain offered to them. Let the price of wheat be the same here as it is in the world market and the nonsense of paying farmers a pension of thousands of pounds every year not to work would come to an end immediately. Disentangling ourselves from the CAP would stop the war now being fought between the forces of destruction and conservation, with both sides paid for out of the public purse. In this matter the economist and the ecologist are running in tandem.

Will things get better if we just leave them alone? Far from it. The economic pressures of the present policy are forcing all farmers throughout the Common Market to go on raising output, which means of course increasing the inputs. And just as the Continental farmer is behind us in output, he is also behind us in inputs – the use of pesticides, herbicides and nitrates, the amalgamation of fields by taking down hedges, the draining of land and all the other steps taken by us to achieve maximum yields, regardless of the effect upon the environment. If our farmers are to keep ahead – or even abreast – in this race, they will have to go on increasing their inputs. The Continental farmer, starting from a lower plane, can afford to stay behind his British counterpart, and so he will be doing less damage to the environment. One might call it an 'ecological damage gap'. It follows that the CAP as it now is will do more harm to our countryside, cause more pollution and bring more danger to the health of our livestock, our wildlife and ourselves than it will on the Continent.

The fifth argument stems from the natural conflict of agricultural interests between the ten countries. This is why there are lamb wars, turkey wars, fish wars, cauliflower wars, wine wars and all the kerfuffle about UHT milk. Why do people take hold of a bottle of precious claret and pour the contents down the drain, vowing never again to drink wine from France? Why do Renault salesmen get accosted on the forecourt with abuse about 'buying French'? The Common Agricultural Policy does not serve the cause of European unity. It does the opposite. It causes friction and irritation. The constant rows and bickering between Ministers in Brussels are far from the ideals of Monnet and Adenauer.

So, despite what Robert Jackson and others may say, these five arguments provide plenty of scope for negotiation. The aim should be an end to the pretence that an agricultural policy can be common and uniform throughout ten disparate countries and still be in the interests of both the farmers and the consumers in them all. A case for coordinating our respective policies and cooperating together on a number of agricultural issues can well be made out, but that is something quite different from a single Common Agricultural Policy pervading the lives of 250 million people. By all means let us agree together not to use certain pesticides – as we have done already – and take other steps that are manifestly in the interests of all farmers and all consumers; but the number of occasions when the interests of 250 million people converge completely are not many, and they are not enough to warrant the attempts at a common policy.

As so much of the Common Market turns upon the Common Agricultural Policy and so many comfortable jobs in Brussels are at stake, we can be sure that intense pressure will be applied to prevent us withdrawing from the CAP. Our withdrawal would, of course, cause its demise in its present form. Compromise would be sought in a botched-up arrangement to keep the CAP going a few years longer, but this would be short sighted. The troubles of the CAP are too deep seated to go away with a little tinkering. Besides, almost any form of tinkering – like a tax on nitrogen use – will bear more heavily on our farmers than the others. So it comes back to being a question of will. The British people, through the British government, must be determined to put it right by the only way feasible – the repatriation of agricultural policy. Let the negotiations be carried on in a spirit of reason and neighbourliness. There is no need for any unpleasantness between ourselves and the Nine. Once it is clear to them that we are resolved to withdraw from the CAP, they will have no alternative but to facilitate our leaving. They would gain nothing from any discord.

Repatriating agricultural policy will be like stepping over a stile and getting into a wide open field where we are free to devise whatever policy for farming we find most in tune with the interests of our own farmers, taxpayers and consumers. It will be a policy that looks after our countryside and its distinctive features; it will also pay heed to our allies in the Commonwealth and the United States and to the needs of the Third World. It will be a policy that does not overlook the needs of our other industries and the utter waste caused by having more than three million men and women out of work. It will be an agricultural policy radically different from what is today thought to be in the interests of Continental Europe.

Our own Parliament will then regain both the right and the power to pass a new Agriculture Act. One of the first sections of the Act should lay down the principle that the farmer is a businessman, as much as the grocer, the corn merchant or the fertiliser manufacturer. Like any other businessman he is then free to produce what he wishes and free to sell it at the highest price he can get. What price he charges and what profit he makes are matters between his customer and himself. The rest of us should not interfere.

Having put the farmer on that solid rock, the Act should go on to state that we are entitled to interfere in other ways. Every businessman in a modern society is called upon to conform to a host of laws, some irksome, others out of date or superfluous, but most of them reasonable. Now we come to where the farmer should be privileged; and here we stop calling agriculture 'an industry' and look upon it as something much more precious. Unlike an industry, its own good health cannot be set apart from the health of all of us. Those who look after the millions of cattle, sheep, pigs and hens have their lives in their hands; and at least a moral duty exists to treat them for what they are, sentient creatures. There is the landscape too. Our countryside, other than the upper reaches of Snowdonia and suchlike places, looks as it does because it is the handiwork of farmers over many generations.

The countryside meant little to those of our forebears who worked sixteen hours a day in a cotton mill, six days a week, and spent most of Sunday in chapel. The transformation in the life of the British family must be recognised by this new Agriculture Act. The ordinary family now owns a car and, come the weekend, can travel many miles to escape the concrete jungle of the inner city or the lesser jungle of suburbia. Millions and millions of pensioners and others made redundant or retired early can make the same journey. It is incontrovertible that though a majority of the British people once had little or no chance to see, let alone explore, England's countryside, now they do. Yet the irony of it is that the quality, beauty and amenities of our countryside grow less as the number who seek them grows more. Farmers should catch at this irony. They should argue that they do not wish to see this loss, but they cannot afford to do what they themselves would like to do, so long as farming is made into aggro-culture. Let farmers be paid for what they are – the caretakers of the countryside, the people who make it and shape it – so that they can take care of it.

'Good husbandry' may be a vague term, and its standards may change over the years; what is 'good' in the eyes of one generation may be indifferent, out of date or even 'bad' to their grandchildren. To use artificial fertilisers or pesticides may be questionable, but it would be foolish legislation to prohibit the use of them all. Some are dangerous and their use in this country or in others is illegal; some are safe in some circumstances and their use has to be regulated. The law on the subject needs to be readily changed to adapt to new discoveries of science, whether of new aids for the farmer or new dangers both to him and the rest of us.

Soil is a priceless thing. Sterilising it, impregnating it with poisons, to the point when it could no longer grow food for us would be bad enough, though other countries could come to our aid and feed us instead; but the death of plants, trees, birds, and other living creatures cannot be made good. The farmers, as caretakers of the land, are the most important people living in our country. They must be treated as such if they are to take care of it.

Thus the new Act should make clear the supreme importance of agriculture. In doing so, it should strike a bargain for farmers as well as for the rest of us. In deciding *what* he is to produce and in marketing it, he must be left alone to do what he considers profitable; but the Act should also lay down the principles about *how* it should be produced. The public would thus have a right to interfere when methods of farming conflict with any one of the following:

*The beauty and quality of the landscape;
*The welfare of farm animals;
*The health of the nation;
*Good husbandry.

In each case, whenever the public through the legislative process prevented the farmer pursuing his profit, there would be a prima face case for compensation. Obviously, not on every occasion would the public be expected to pay money to the farmer as a businessman, for all manner of ingenious and whimsical schemes would be mooted to extract public money. So the details of the new policy would have to be a matter for delegated legislation in the form of Statutory Instruments to be introduced or amended or repealed with reasonable speed.

The Act would set the scene for the reconciliation of the interests of farmer, landowner, taxpayer, consumer, conservationist and welfarist. The NFU and the Friends of the Earth would sit in the same canoe, both paddling in the same direction. It sounds a tall order to reconcile so many, but what has to be emphasised is that the present system, so long as it goes on, is forcing the farmer and landowner further apart from the rest of the public. This must be highly dangerous for those who farm in good faith.

The new principles must be so clearly understood by the Ministry of Agriculture that it is purged of the over-riding desire, intensified in the years 1979-1983, to urge our farmers to maximum production, regardless of cost to themselves or anyone else. I believe we will one day look back upon them as black years, when farming went awry through no fault of the farmer himself.

It goes without saying that this new policy would bring to an end the dumping of our home-produced food onto the world market with the aid of public money. If done at all, it would be out of the speculator's pocket. The other members of the EEC might continue with the common policy, but our withdrawal would so deplete its funds that it is unlikely that the system of intervention buying and the selling of food abroad with export subsidies would carry on, except on a modest scale. This should give the developing countries a better chance of exporting onto the world market. It would also enable the low-cost food producers of the world, especially New Zealand, Australia, Canada and the United States, to have a fair share of the world market.

The policy would also remove the main obstacle that prevents the British people from eating the food of their choice – the taxes on food entering our ports. Whether some kind of countervailing duty should remain on food imported from countries that continue to subsidise their agriculture is debatable; probably it should, as it would then be an inducement for those countries to apply principles similar to our own. Once disentangled from the Common Agricultural Policy, we would be able to make and enforce our own anti-dumping regulations.

Then there is the whole range of grants from either our own Exchequer or the Guidance Fund of the CAP that are intended to raise output. They cost many millions of pounds and are a large item of expenditure by the Ministry of Agriculture. According to its Supply Estimates for 1983-1984 the total provision for its work was no less than £1,026 millions, of which only £93 millions was attributable to non-agricultural spending on fishing and forestry. The Estimates set out the details of the Ministry's expenditure and run to over thirty pages, but a few items can be listed here:

Guidance Premium for Beef and Sheep Production	£ 1,288,000
Agriculture and Horticulture Development Scheme	£49,852,000
Agriculture and Horticulture Grant Scheme	£78,000,000
Grants for the Encouragement of Cooperation	£ 2,902,000
Grants for Pasteurisation Equipment	£ 91,000
Grants for the Improvement of Farm Structures (under EEC Directive)	£ 111,000
Grants for the Improvement of Farm Structures for Ministry Approved Amalgamations	£ 218,000
Farm Accounts Grants	£ 1,057,000
Guarantees for Bank Loans for Agricultural Businesses	£ 235,000
Aids to Assist Less Favoured Farming Areas	£31,961,000
Veterinary Inspections	£ 9,821,000
Land Drainage Grants	£36,723,000
Agricultural Training Board	£ 7,616,000
Food from Britain Grant	£ 3,872,000

And a total of about £140 millions for research into increasing production.

Assuming that about £300 millions could be saved by bringing to an end all grants and subsidies intended to increase output, a similar sum could be made available to farmers to compensate them in the four circumstances given above. As much money as before could be given to agriculture, but it would be distributed in such a way that the kind of farmer who gets the least now might get a great deal more, and vice versa. The grants would be for the benefit of both taxpayer and farmer.

Once we went over to this alternative system, I believe those clashes that now take place constantly and increasingly would begin to diminish. High-input/high-output farming causes those clashes; going down to a lower gear will reverse the trend. Incidentally, the grants cost the public over £1,000 per farmer. As they tend to benefit the larger farmer rather than his smaller neighbour, their value is of little significance to the former's income, but the alternative system would improve the income of a small farmer and go a long way towards helping him to survive.

This alternative system of grants might eliminate most of the farming practices that are questioned on grounds of ethics, health, and good husbandry. If prohibitions were also considered necessary, then it would be right to prohibit the import of food from those countries which continued the practice we had ended. For example, once we made use of 245T illegal here, as it is in other countries, we should place an embargo upon imports from where it is still allowed. There is no doubt that Denmark, whose share of our bacon market provides a livelihood for thousands of farmers, would abolish sow stalls if we were to make them illegal and also prohibit the import of pigmeat from countries which still used them. My visits to Danish farms convinced me that they have felt compelled to adopt our intensive methods simply to compete with us. So it might be said that our system has exported to Denmark a practice that every right-minded stockman would condemn as cruelty. Their laws relating to animal welfare are far ahead of ours. For example, the keeping of hens in battery cages was made illegal in Denmark long ago, though because they are in the Common Market, they are not now enforcing the law.

There is one major advantage of being a food-importing nation: it can impose standards on other countries by prohibiting certain practices within its own country and then prohibiting imports from others that continue with them.

Next, the whole field of tax relief and tax allowances for agriculture needs to be reviewed. They promote too many bad practices and penalise good ones. They favour the already rich farmer, and they handicap the beginner. The cost to us is no less than £930 millions (*Hansard*, 24 October 1983).

There is a place for commodity agreements between other countries and ourselves. They can be to the commercial advantage of both. The Commonwealth Sugar Agreement proved its worth; every cane-growing country would be glad to see the return of some similar arrangement. There is no valid reason for Queensland to be excluded.

Lastly, there must be one most important form of import control. An integral part of a free trade policy is a floating exchange rate. It is the ingredient that makes free trade also fair trade, and it prevents any competent producer being placed at a disadvantage. Not only is it the most efficient import control; it always operates naturally in accordance with what the customer really wants – as distinct from what a government thinks he should have – and so it never works arbitrarily. When the country is importing more than it is exporting, its currency falls in value automatically; and the more it devalues, the dearer its imports become. Its own products also become more competitive in the domestic market as a result. At the same time, they become cheaper in the world market because fewer pounds must be purchased in the foreign exchange market in order to buy them. The converse is the case when a country's exports exceed its imports. The impersonal forces at work in the foreign exchange market make sure that the cost of importing its goods goes up. This kind of import control is of particular advantage to agriculture, and it serves as a perfect corset of protection.

These measures would not, and could not, take us back to dog-and-stick farming. Apart from anything else, it is technically and physically impossible for that to happen, as an earlier chapter explained. Besides, there can be no question of trying to go backwards; on the contrary, we must move forward to use our own natural resources (not just our land) and that of other countries in a more sensible way than we do today. Our planet is large enough, and nature has made it rich enough, to sustain every human being, and wildlife too, but not if we persist in misusing its resources. The only way, it seems to me, that we can make the best use of those resources is by a free trade policy, subject to the safeguards given above. The policy would go a long way towards changing the places where food is grown in the world, from where it is grown at high cost to where it can be grown at a lower cost, ecologically as well as economically. We know too little of the ecological damage we are doing with our present policy to make any estimate of the cost, yet what little we know is enough to show that the damage is being done at a quickening speed.

The policy of changing gear would also afford a system that is self-correcting, in contrast to what is now self-destructing. In the last twelve months I have spoken on these themes to about forty audiences of farmers; and though there was at first a lot of doubt, both about my analysis of why agricultural policy had gone wrong and about the alternative, there seems now to be an acceptance of the analysis. The remedial medicine is unpalatable to a generation of farmers who have been conditioned by politicians to grow the maximum. Farmers have good cause to be fearful of the unknown. The fear of foreclosure, the humiliation of failure, the selling-up of a farm and all the stock, the search for another livelihood, all that can fill a farmer with foreboding when someone talks of another policy. The devil you know is likely to be a better companion than the one you have yet to meet, but the particular devil I am attacking is getting more devilish and more destructive. The longer we stay in his clutches, the more painful it will be to get out. To make the change, what farmers need now is a blend of qualities that enabled their forebears, generations ago, to overcome what faced them: foresight and resilience and faith and, most important of all, courage.